ALAN HANSEN'S
SOCCER QUIZ BOOK

ALAN HANSEN'S
SOCCER QUIZ BOOK

ALAN HANSEN
WITH WILLIAM WALKER

CollinsWillow
An Imprint of HarperCollins*Publishers*

First published in 1993 by
Collins Willow
an imprint of HarperCollins*Publishers*
London

© William Walker 1993

A CIP catalogue record for this book
is available from the British Library

ISBN 0 00 218528 8

Printed and bound in Great Britain by
Cox & Wyman Ltd

CONTENTS

INTRODUCTION

Quizzes are great fun – we often played them on the team bus when we were travelling to away matches.

I used to do fairly well and I also gained a bit of a reputation for remembering matches that we played ourselves. In actual fact, some of the lads called me 'The Memory Man' since I could usually tell them when we won a particular trophy, who we beat on the way and even who we played the next week!

Well, this book gives you the perfect opportunity to see how much you've picked up. I've been in some knowledgeable company with William Walker, who's a real football quiz expert, and we've put together some 1,200 questions on all aspects of the game.

The questions are split into 20 different sections – each based on a particular topic or theme. At the end of each section you can gauge how well you did with our special ratings system.

Some questions are definitely easier than others and, if you're stumped, the answers are all there at the back of the book.

So get stuck in and while you're at it, why not challenge your family or friends to a bit of fun competition?

Best of luck...

Alan Hansen

<u>1</u>
<u>THE PREMIER</u>
<u>LEAGUE</u>

*'We saw a lot of exciting games in the first-ever
Premier League and, from Christmas onwards, both
Manchester United and Aston Villa played some fantastic stuff
– especially at home. The overall standard of football was not
at all bad but less teams and therefore less games would
obviously help improve that.'*

1. Which team's 1–0 victory at Villa Park on May 2 enabled Manchester United to claim the inaugural Premier League title?

2. Can you name the Norwich manager who led his club into a European place for the first time in their history?

3. Who scored the Premier League's first-ever goal?

4. Which team failed to win any of their away League matches in 1992–93?

5. Nottingham Forest lost their Premier League status after going down 2–0 at home to which fellow relegation strugglers?

6. The management duo of Ray Clemence and Doug Livermore guided which club's first Premier League campaign?

7. Who trounced high-flying Norwich 7–1 in October 1992?

8. What shirt number was worn by Premier stars Chris Waddle and Ian Wright in 1992–93?

9. In December 1992, who became only the second player to score for both clubs in Merseyside derby matches?

10. Trevor Francis was one of the '92–93 Premier League's two player-managers – who was the other?

11. Name the two Ipswich Town players who represented Canada in the qualifying competition for the 1994 World Cup.

12. Who scored twice for Aston Villa against his old club Liverpool in September 1992?

13. Which Liverpool striker missed an open goal in that match at Villa Park?

14. Which team led the Premier table at the end of 1992?

15. Selhurst Park is the current home of which Premier League side?

16. Frenchman Eric Cantona fired the Premier League's first-ever hat-trick – against which team?

17. Which of the London clubs finished highest in '92–93?

18. Who is the Chief Executive of the Premier League?

19. How many goals did Mark Hughes score in Manchester United's Championship campaign?

20. Who were the lowest scoring side in the 1992–93 Premier League?

21. Name the three goalkeepers used by Liverpool during '92–93.

22. Who scored two hat-tricks in the space of three days over the 1993 Easter holiday?

23. Which club flew a plane-load of fans to a Monday night away fixture at Oldham in November?

24. Goalkeeper Mark Bosnich helped Aston Villa to second place in the '92–93 Premier League. What nationality is he?

25. Who was the first Premier League manager to be sacked?

26. What promise did Ian Wright break when he netted in Arsenal's away match at Crystal Palace in November 1992?

27. What is the usual colour worn by Premier League referees?

28. Who scored the last goal of Manchester United's successful League campaign?

29. Can you name the two Zimbabwean internationals who appeared in the '92–93 Premier League?

30. Against which team did Alan Shearer bag two goals on his Blackburn debut?

31. Which was the first Premier League match to be screened 'live' on Sky Sports?

32. Which team began the 1992–93 season as the bookmakers' favourites to win the Premier League?

33. Which Premier League striker scored a World Cup goal against Manchester United goalkeeper Peter Schmeichel in April 1993?

34. Which was the last team to lose their unbeaten record in the 1992–93 season?

35. What were the results of the two Merseyside derbies of '92–93?

36. Where did champions Leeds crash 4–0 in November?

37. Who was Southampton's top League scorer for 1992–93?

38. Which Premier League manager missed his side's best performance of the season – a 6–2 trouncing of Spurs on the last day – because he was scouting at the Coventry v Leeds match?

39. Which Premier side introduced a new away strip of salmon pink and navy blue stripes at the start of '92–93?

40. Which Championship-chasing Aston Villa player had already won League title medals with Everton and Arsenal?

41. How many London derby games were contested during 1992–93?

42. Which Everton player was ordered off twice during the season?

43. Given that they finished third in the '92–93 table, what was remarkable about Norwich City's goal difference?

44. In 1992–93, Paul Wilkinson scored 14 League goals for which relegated team?

45. Which team scored four goals in four minutes at home to Southampton in February 1993?

46. In October 1992, who broke his club's all-time scoring record when he netted his first goal in ten attempts against Manchester United at Old Trafford?

47. Oldham retained their Premier League status by defeating which side 4–3 at home on the last day of the '92–93 season?

48. Both '92–93 Sheffield derby matches finished with the same scoreline – what was it?

49. Vinnie Jones has appeared for two clubs in the Premier League. Wimbledon is one – who is the other?

50. In which year will the Premier League be cut to 20 teams?

51. Can you name the Spurs starlet who is the Premier League's youngest scorer?

52. Did Arsenal top the table at any stage of 1992–93?

53. Which Manchester United star missed the early part of the '92–93 season because he was suffering from viral meningitis?

54. Who took over from Gordon Strachan as captain of Leeds?

55. At which ground could an ordinary supporter have paid as much as £30 to watch Premier League football in 1992–93?

56. Prior to 1993, when did Swindon Town last play in England's top division?

57. Which team handed Manchester United their biggest League defeat of 1992–93?

58. Which striker hit nine Premier League goals for Chelsea before departing for Sunderland in November 1992?

59. Which Premier League team picked up the most yellow and red cards throughout 1992–93 – Sheffield United, Southampton or Wimbledon?

60. What was special about the Manchester City v QPR clash of 17th August 1992?

How you fared...

46–60	Just champion!
31–45	Serious challengers
16–30	Relegation worries
0–15	Sack the board!

2
FORWARD
THINKING

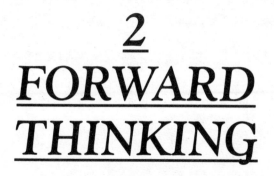

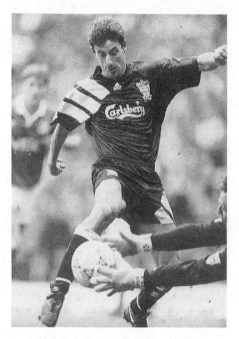

*'I played centre-forward for Partick Thistle reserves a couple of times but didn't fancy it much – you get kicked too often!
For me, Rush, Lineker and Aldridge were great exponents of forward play – they had the instinct to get into the right position every time.'*

1. Who was the FA Premier League's leading goalscorer in 1992–93?

2. How many goals has Ian Wright scored in FA Cup Finals?

3. In 1992–93, who scored over 50 goals in matches for Rangers and Scotland despite being unable to complete the season because of a broken leg?

4. Name the two leading European sides for which Mark Hughes has played.

5. Who was West Ham United's top goalscorer in the years between 1966 and 1971?

6. From which fellow Yorkshire club did Sheffield Wednesday sign David Hirst?

7. Ian Rush netted his record-breaking 24th goal for Wales against which country in March 1993?

8. Who was the English First Division's leading goalscorer on six occasions between 1959 and 1969?

9. Can you name the former Brentford striker who hit 19 League goals for Wimbledon in his debut season in the top flight?

10. Between 1985 and 1992, Frank McAvennie enjoyed two fruitful spells at which London club?

11. Which striker won both a League Championship and World Cup winner's medal in 1966?

12. In 1992–93, who scored 12 goals in 11 starts for Newcastle following his £1.75 million move from Bristol City?

13. Which prolific goalscorer of the 1970s was nicknamed 'Supermac'?

14. How many times did Portsmouth's Guy Whittingham find the net in the 1992–93 Barclays' First Division – 22, 32 or 42?

15. Who netted 349 goals for Everton in the years between 1925 and 1937?

16. In October 1992, who broke a leg – 245 minutes into his career at Manchester United and missed the remainder of The Reds' title-winning season?

17. Which former Liverpool star hit 21 League goals for Tranmere in 1992–93?

18. Name the two players who jointly hold the scoring record for the Scottish national team.

19. Bob Taylor was the leading marksman in the '92–93 Second Division. For which club was he on target 29 times?

20. Despite being a regular club goalscorer since 1983, this player didn't score for his country until his 26th international, in the 1992 European Championship finals in Sweden. Who is he?

21. What nationality is Bontcho Guentchev?

22. Which striker blasted a hat-trick in the 1992 Charity Shield match?

23. In May 1993, where did Ian Wright net his first goal for England after coming on as a substitute?

24. Who scored ten goals in six games for Coventry after joining the Sky Blues from Newcastle in 1992?

25. England's record goalscorer Bobby Charlton played League football for two clubs. Manchester United was one – can you name the other?

26. He was Tottenham's leading scorer in the 1984–85 and '85–86 seasons and he has also played for Watford and QPR. Who is he?

27. In June 1992, Gary Lineker was controversially withdrawn in last match for England. Which striker replaced him?

28. Who was the first Northern Ireland international forward to hit 100 League goals in England?

29. Name the striker who scored in every round of the 1992 FA Cup except the Final – when he missed a glorious chance to put his team in front.

30. Who scored his 100th League goal for Walsall against Hereford in August 1992 – 13 years after netting his first as a 17-year-old for Wolves?

31. Against which team did Aston Villa's Dalian Atkinson score the 1992–93 Premier League's 'Goal of the Season'?

32. Who bagged a nap hand of five goals for the Football League against the Irish League in Belfast in 1959?

33. Who topped the Third, Second and First Division goalscoring charts in consecutive seasons from 1983 to 1985?

34. For which team did Kevin Keegan score the more goals as a player – Southampton or Newcastle?

35. Who was the Arsenal winger who bagged 33 goals during the 1932–33 season?

36. Which former Celtic striker caused a furore in 1989 by signing for arch-rivals Rangers?

37. Before Matt Le Tissier became an England B cap, which international manager watched him with a view to selecting him for his team?

38. Who holds the record for the most goals in a single season for England?

39. Which leading Premier League striker was branded a 'hopeless footballer' by the then-Swansea manager John Bond in 1985?

40. Despite his injury, Alan Shearer was Blackburn's leading goalscorer for '92–93 with 22 goals in all competitions. But which former Leicester City striker hit 21 for the Ewood Park side?

41. About whom was Wolves manager Graham Turner speaking when he said in 1988: 'People say his first touch isn't good, but he usually scores with his second!'?

42. This striker won 52 England caps and played, amongst others, for Atalanta, Birmingham City and Detroit Express. Who is he?

43. Charlie Buchan scored a record 209 goals for which club before becoming a soccer journalist?

44. Who was Ipswich Town's top scorer in the '92–93 Premier League?

45. Which former Welsh international striker was nicknamed 'The Gentle Giant'?

46. Francis Lee was which club's leading goalscorer between 1970 and 1974?

47. On the same Saturday in October 1983, two First Division strikers banged in five goals away from home. Ian Rush was one – who was the other?

48. Gary Lineker's first-ever striking partner for England was with AC Milan at the time. Can you name him?

49. For which team did Kenny Dalglish score the more league goals – Celtic or Liverpool?

50. At which club did Mark Bright begin his career?

51. Name the Everton striker who earned £10,000 from a national newspaper for hitting 30 League goals in 1977–78.

52. What was Peter Beardsley's first League club?

53. Did Liverpool make a profit or loss on Dean Saunders when they off-loaded him to Aston Villa in September 1992?

54. Paul Mariner won 33 of his 35 England caps at which club?

55. In which decade did Joe Payne etch his place in the record books by blasting ten goals for Luton against Bristol Rovers in a Third Division (South) fixture?

56. Mark Hateley's father was a prolific scorer for many clubs in the 1960s and '70s. Can you name him?

57. Who was the Scottish League's leading goalscorer in 1984 and 1987?

58. Robert Rosario was on target for which two clubs in the 1992–93 Premier League?

59. Who was the last striker to win the PFA Player of the Year award?

60. Gary Lineker hit 40 goals in his one-and-only season with Everton. What was the season?

How you fared...

46–60	Deadly finishing!
31–45	Accurate shooting
16–30	Need sharpening up
0–15	Watch those photographers!

3
THE WORLD CUP

'I took part in the 1982 World Cup and enjoyed the experience – especially playing against that famous Brazil side which included Zico, Socrates and Junior. It's important we have a good World Cup in the USA, with plenty of attacking football – there's been too much defensive stuff in recent tournaments.'

1. During season 1992–93, England won two home games in their 1994 World Cup qualifying section. Which countries did they defeat?

2. Who scored a goal aided by the so-called 'Hand of God' in the 1986 World Cup tournament?

3. Which is the only stadium to have hosted the World Cup Final on two separate occasions?

4. Two nations won all three of their first round matches in the 1990 World Cup finals. Italy was one – can you name the other?

5. Who scored for Scotland in three successive final tournaments between 1974 and 1982?

6. In which year did England go out of the World Cup finals despite playing five matches undefeated?

7. What unwelcome World Cup 'first' did Chile's Carlos Caszely achieve during the 1974 match against West Germany?

8. Against which country did Jimmy Greaves score his one and only World Cup finals goal?

9. Can you name any two of the three European countries which have played in the Final twice but lost on both occasions?

10. In the 1966 World Cup, which competing team's players had an average height of less than 5 ft 7 inches?

11. Which team once scored a goal in the Final before any of the opposing side had touched the ball?

12. Who is the oldest player to score in the finals?

13. In 1990, which country reached the quarter-finals of the tournament without having won a match from open play?

14. Where will the 1998 tournament be held?

15. Pele is the only man to have played for three World Cup winning sides. But, in which year did he miss the final stages of the tournament through injury?

16. How many 'repeat' World Cup Finals have there been? (i.e. the same teams meeting as had contested the Final of four years previously)

17. Can you name the Italian striker who was the leading goalscorer in the 1982 World Cup?

18. What World Cup result of 3 June 1978 did pop singer Rod Stewart describe as 'Endsville'?

19. Who was the first player to score in every round of a finals tournament?

20. Which of these Premier League grounds staged matches in the 1966 World Cup – Anfield, St James' Park or Hillsborough?

21. Who scored the only goal of the Brazil v Argentina second round clash in the 1990 finals?

22. How many different World Cup medals did Franz Beckenbauer win during his playing days?

23. Which was the first African team to win a game in the finals – Cameroon, Morocco or Tunisia?

24. What rare and distinguished feat have Paul Breitner, Pele and Vava all achieved?

25. Which British player has appeared in more World Cup finals matches than any other?

26. David Platt headed two goals in Italia '90 – name either of England's opponents.

27. In which year were the finals first transmitted in colour on UK television?

28. Against which country did Northern Ireland's Pat Jennings make his farewell World Cup appearance in 1986?

29. Can you name the twin brothers who appeared in Holland's 1978 World Cup Final line–up?

30. In 1958, who only came into his country's World Cup side as a late replacement for fellow striker Rene Biliard but went on to set a new record for the most goals in a single tournament?

31. What number was Martin Peters wearing when he netted for England against West Germany in the 1966 World Cup Final?

32. What was notable and impressive about Iraq's qualification for the 1986 tournament in Mexico?

33. How many of the Republic of Ireland's 1990 World Cup squad played their club football outside of the Emerald Isle?

34. Which was the first European country to stage the finals?

35. Which member of Brazil's winning side of 1970 played against Italy in the 1978 third place play–off?

36. Gary Lineker scored six of England's goals in the 1986 World Cup. Who scored the other and which club was he with at that time?

37. Who was the last manager to lead to a team other than his native country to the World Cup Final?

38. How many players were red-carded during the 1990 finals – 12, 14 or 16?

39. Five months before England defeated West Germany in the 1966 Final, the teams had met in a midweek Wembley friendly. What was the score?

40. Can you name the Hungarian substitute who notched a hat-trick against El Salvador in only nine minutes of a 1982 first round match?

41. Which West German midfielder marked Diego Maradona in the 1986 Final in Mexico City?

42. Name either of the Italian cities which had brand-new stadia constructed especially for the 1990 tournament.

43. Who was the qualified doctor who skippered Brazil in the 1982 and 1986 tournaments?

44. Which country reached the Final of the World Cup after eliminating Scotland in a qualifying round play-off?

45. Who scored for Wales in their 1–1 draw against the RCS in Ostrava during the 1994 qualifying competition?

46. Winners Argentina lost only one match of the 1978 tournament. Which country defeated them?

47. What part did Naranjito and Pique play in the 1982 and 1986 World Cup finals respectively?

48. In which year did the national team of the now-abolished state of East Germany make their one and only appearance in the finals?

49. Who was the first man to score for England in two consecutive World Cup tournaments?

50. This team scored the quickest goal of Italia '90 but are highly-unlikely ever to appear in another World Cup competition. Who are they?

51. In 1993, which European country qualified for the finals for the first time since joining FIFA in 1927?

52. What unusual colour of jerseys did the Italian side wear in their 1938 quarter-final clash with host nation France?

53. The *ola* became a prominent feature of the 1986 tournament. What was it?

54. Tomas Skuhravy was one of only two hat-trick scorers in the 1990 finals. In which match did he bag his three goals?

55. How many of the 1986 quarter-final matches were decided on a penalty shoot-out?

56. Which teams contested the infamous 1954 match which became known as 'The Battle of Berne'?

57. How many of their 22-man squad did France use during the 1978 tournament?

58. Name the beaten semi-finalists in 1986.

59. Who was the last winning captain to lift the World Cup in his own club stadium?

60. Which 21-year-old Argentinian player was ordered off against Brazil in 1982?

How you fared...

46–60	Top of the world!
31–45	In the medals
16–30	First round make-weights
0–15	Failed to qualify

4
CLUB CALL

*'There is definitely more pressure on playing for a big club –
particularly the likes of Liverpool – because you tend to become
victims of your own success. We had a spell when we were
pushing for the Double almost every year and it becomes
very difficult to better that.'*

1. Which club made an emotional return to their old ground of The Valley in December 1992?

2. Who is the multi-millionaire benefactor of Blackburn Rovers?

3. Manchester United fielded international players from how many different countries during 1992–93?

4. At which club did David Platt, Geoff Thomas and Rob Jones all establish their senior football careers?

5. Which Premier League club was once known as Ardwick FC?

6. Which was the first English side to reach a half century of goals during the 1992–93 season?

7. Who is Aston Villa's leading goalscorer of all time?

8. Name Merseyside's Endsleigh League club.

9. Which was the first club to win the League and Cup 'Double' in England?

10. Which club resigned from the Barclays League at the start of the 1992–93 season?

11. Everton last played in the Second Division during which decade?

12. Which team set a club record of seven successive away victories by winning at Grimsby in December 1992?

13. Which side lost 7–1 at Exeter in what proved to be their last Football League match in 1972?

14. Did Doncaster Rovers ever play in the old First Division?

15. Which European trophy have Manchester United and Manchester City both won?

16. Who are known as the Posh?

17. True or false – Nottingham Forest have never won the FA Cup?

18. Which Midlands team lost in the First Division (formerly Second Division) play-off final for the second successive season in 1993?

19. Which is the only member club of the original Football League not currently playing in either the Premiership or the Endsleigh League?

20. Kevin Hector holds the appearance record for which club?

21. Which two English clubs have supplied European Footballers of the Year?

22. In which decade did Huddersfield Town win three consecutive League Championships?

23. Which was the last Welsh club to play in the old First Division?

24. Roger Palmer is which club's all-time top scorer?

25. Colchester United enjoyed their best-ever FA Cup run in 1971 – which round did they reach?

26. Which famous club plummeted from the First to the Fourth Division between 1984 and 1986?

27. Which team has won the more Birmingham derby matches – Aston Villa or Birmingham City?

28. Who did Bruce Grobbelaar succeed as Liverpool's regular goalkeeper?

29. Which club's name once had the prefix 'Burslem'?

30. John Trollope made 770 League appearances for which club between 1960 and 1980?

31. York City won the 1993 Third Division play-offs – which team did they defeat in the final at Wembley?

32. Which was the first British club to 'go public' by selling shares on the stock exchange?

33. Which is the older Sheffield club – United or Wednesday?

34. Who is 'Deadly Doug' to Aston Villa fans?

35. Which club won the inaugural Konica League of Wales?

36. Which team set a club record of 25 unbeaten League games before going down 1–0 at Leyton Orient in February 1993?

37. What was the nickname of Crystal Palace before they became 'The Eagles'?

38. Name the famous Bolton Wanderers striker who later became club president.

39. Which was the first club to automatically lose their League status as a result of finishing bottom of Division Four?

40. What are the colours of Northampton Town?

41. Which of the following Lancashire clubs have played in a major European club tournament – Blackpool, Bolton Wanderers or Burnley?

42. For which South Coast club have Darren Anderton, Mick Quinn and Neil Webb all played?

43. Who did Gerry Francis succeed as QPR manager in 1991?

44. Which club were once Boscombe St John's?

45. Which of the Bristol clubs have played in England's top division?

46. Until 1970, who were Bradford City's nearest neighbours in the Football League?

47. Which First Division club had eleven internationals on their books during 1962–63?

48. Have Coventry City ever taken part in European competition?

49. American international Kasey Keller kept goal in 45 First Division matches for which club in 1992–93?

50. Leicester City have appeared in four FA Cup Finals since 1949. How many have they won?

51. Which North-Eastern club wasn't managed by an Englishman until 1957?

52. What was the previous name of Swansea City?

53. The book *Biscuits and Royals* tells the history of which club?

54. Which Midlands team won the League Championship three times during the 1950s?

55. In which year did Scarborough make their Football League debut?

56. Electronics company JVC are major sponsors of which leading English club?

57. Which of these clubs has never supplied a full international player to any of the home countries – Chester, Darlington or Rotherham?

58. Wrexham's most-capped player kept goal 28 times for Wales during his time at the club. Can you name him?

59. Which team spent the more seasons in the old First Division – Manchester United or Manchester City?

60. Besides Spurs or Arsenal, which was the last London club to win a major trophy?

How you fared...

46–60	A major force
31–45	Sleeping giant
16–30	Struggling outfit
0–15	Cinderella club

5
SOCCER IN
EUROPE

*'I was so happy at Liverpool that a move to European football
was never something I considered – even though some people
say I may have been suited to the continental-style sweeper
system. I think, however, to operate effectively in the sweeper
system, you need to have played it from early in life.'*

1. Can you name the unfashionable side from La Coruna who were surprise challengers for the 1993 Spanish League?

2. In which Belgian town does the team called Cercle play?

3. The KNVB is the head footballing body of which western European country?

4. Who was the most expensive player in European football during the 1992–93 season?

5. What is the Ukraine's leading club side?

6. Striker Stephane Chapuisat helped Borussia Dortmund knock Celtic out of the 1992–93 UEFA Cup. What nationality is he?

7. Which team clinched their 22nd Belgian League Championship title in 1993?

8. In 1992, German international striker Jurgen Klinsmann left Inter Milan to join which French club?

9. Which Dutch side play their home matches in the Philips Stadion?

10. Who skippered Denmark's 1992 European Championship-winning side?

11. Can you name the Norwegian international who has twice been voted best overseas player in Germany's Bundesliga while playing with Werder Bremen?

12. Who is the most successful manager in the entire history of Spanish club Real Sociedad?

13. Can you name any two of the three Frenchmen to have won the European Footballer of the Year award?

14. Dennis Bergkamp won a UEFA Cup medal with which club in 1992?

15. By what name, thankfully, is Greek club Athletiki Enosis Konstantinopoulos better known?

16. Which Scandinavian country has the oldest Football Association in mainland Europe?

17. For which Spanish team did German international star Andy Brehme play during 1992–93?

18. Who did Berti Vogts succeed as Germany's national team chief in 1990?

19. Name the Bulgarian striker who was said to have been furious at only finishing second in the 1992 European Footballer of the Year poll.

20. Known as locally as Fradi, this Budapest-based club lost to Leeds United in the 1968 Fairs Cup Final. Who are they?

21. Which European national team suffered 32 straight defeats between May 1980 and April 1985?

22. In which German city do the traditional miners' team of Schalke 04 play?

23. Who was the tough-guy French defender involved in a head-butt incident with England's Stuart Pearce during the 1992 European Championship?

24. Which Baltic country does the team Norma Tallinn hail from?

25. Argentina's World Cup skipper Diego Maradona played for which Spanish side during 1992–93?

26. What was impressive about Hertha Berlin's achievement in reaching the 1993 German Cup Final?

27. Baby-faced striker Tomas Brolin is regularly on target for which national side?

28. Which team swooped to bring Portuguese international star Paulo Futre back from Spain in January 1993?

29. Rotterdam was represented by which two clubs in the 1992–93 Dutch First Division?

30. Who managed Barcelona to the Spanish League championship in 1985?

31. Which leading French side play their home matches in the Parc des Princes?

32. For which Hungarian international did Olympiakos Piraeus pay Eintracht Frankfurt £4.7 million in 1988?

33. Name the Englishman who succeeded Uli Stielike as Switzerland's national manager in 1992.

34. Which European stadium has staged more European club finals than any other?

35. Who was the first East German to play for the unified German team?

36. In 1993, Floriana won the League Championship of which small European country for the 25th time?

37. On which south sea island was French international winger Pascal Vahirua born?

38. Which European national side play in red shirts and green shorts?

39. In which city was the Final of the 1992 European Championship played?

40. By what name were FC Berlin known in the days of the communist regime in East Germany?

41. Which goalkeeper completed a European Cup and European Championship double with PSV and Holland in 1988?

42. If you were watching a League match between Doxa and Xanthi, in which country would you be?

43. Which European national side are nicknamed *Les Diables Rouges* or 'Red Devils'?

44. How did English biology student Tom Griffith leave an impression on Swiss football?

45. During his playing days, Johan Cruyff won domestic League titles with which three clubs?

46. What, in German football, is *ein Elfmeterschiessen*?

47. San Marino's international captain Massimo Bonini played against Liverpool in the 1985 European Cup Final. Which club was he with at that time?

48. Besides Real and Atletico, which other team represented Madrid in the '92–93 Spanish First Division?

49. This former Dynamo Kiev and Soviet Union star was European Footballer of the Year in 1975. In January 1992, he was sacked as coach of Greek side Olympiakos. Can you name him?

50. In which European country are the headquarters of UEFA?

51. Werder Bremen clinched the Bundesliga title on the last day of the 1992–93 season. Which team blew their own chances by only drawing 3–3 at Schalke that day?

52. Spanish international midfielder Jose Miguel Gonzalez Martin del Campo is much better known by what one-word name?

53. Between 1958 and 1991, Albanian club SK Tirana were known as 17 Nentori. What was the significance of that name?

54. Where is the Rasunda Stadium?

55. Can you name Feyenoord's 'Wolf Man'?

56. In June 1993, FC Aarau became champions of which country for the first time in 79 years?

57. Bernd Schuster has played for Barcelona, Real Madrid and Atletico Madrid in Spain – but with which club did he win a Bundesliga Championship medal in his native Germany?

58. Which country has a team called Selena?

59. On which holiday island did Real Madrid lose on the last day of both the 1991–92 and '92–93 seasons, allowing Barcelona to clinch the Spanish Championship each time?

60. Which club lost its Bundesliga place in 1993, after 22 years in the top flight?

How you fared...

46–60	*Ooh La La!*
31–45	*Très bon*
16–30	*Comme ci, comme ça*
0–15	*Hasta la vista, baby!*

<u>6</u>
ENGLAND: THE TEAM

'Recent England managers have had unbelievable criticism from the media and I feel sorry for them. Often, most other managers would pick nine or ten of the same team. However, you're only as good as your results and if England have a bad time results-wise, the manager gets slaughtered.'

1. Who scored on his international debut for England against San Marino in February 1993?

2. Which was the first team to defeat England in a World Cup finals match?

3. Who were the last father-and-son duo to play for England?

4. How many goals did Gary Lineker score during his eight-year international career?

5. Who won the first of his 90 England caps, wearing the No.6 jersey, in a 2–0 Wembley victory over the Republic of Ireland in 1980?

6. What is England's highest finishing position in the European Championship?

7. When England lost 3–1 to Brazil in the quarter-final of the 1962 World Cup, their goal was scored by an Inter Milan player. Who was he?

8. Which Dutch midfielder was involved in the collision which fractured Paul Gascoigne's cheek bone during the 1993 World Cup qualifier at Wembley?

9. In which year did John Salako make his international debut?

10. Who was the first England player to be ordered off in a World Cup tie?

11. Which of these 1970s 'flair-players' won the most caps – Alan Hudson, Peter Osgood or Rodney Marsh?

12. Where did England lose 1–0 in their first match of the 1992–93 season?

13. Who, in June 1993, became the first black player to captain the full England side?

14. Which was the last team to put five goals past England?

15. What was the nickname given to centre-forward Nat Lofthouse after a scintillating two-goal display away to Austria in 1952?

16. Who is England's most-capped outfield player?

17. What injury forced John Barnes to miss the 1992 European Championship finals in Sweden?

18. How many games did England lose in the four years between the 1966 and 1970 World Cup tournaments?

19. Who did Graham Taylor name as England captain in succession to Gary Lineker?

20. What was the result of England's first-ever international – against Scotland in Glasgow in 1872?

21. England's leading goalscorer of the 1978–79 season was at that time based in West German club football – who was he?

22. How many times did England fail to qualify for the World Cup finals between 1950 and 1990?

23. What is the greatest number of players that any one club has supplied for a single England international?

24. How many matches did England win in the 1992 European Championship finals?

25. Which Manchester United starlet made his England debut aged only 18 in 1955?

26. In percentage terms, which England manager had the better record – Bobby Robson or Ron Greenwood?

27. Which of these colours have been used by England as an alternative strip – red, sky blue and yellow?

28. Who was England's leading goalscorer during the season in which they eventually won the World Cup?

29. What was the scoreline in Hungary's famous victory over England at Wembley in 1953?

30. Who made his England debut as a Third Division player in 1989?

31. Which member of the 1966 World Cup winning side regularly played wearing contact lenses and false teeth?

32. Who holds the record for the most hat-tricks for England?

33. When did England last play a Home International Championship match?

34. Who is England's most-capped goalkeeper – after Peter Shilton?

35. How many goals did England lose in the qualifying rounds of the 1990 World Cup?

36. With which club did striker Alan Shearer win his first international cap?

37. Who was the Glasgow-born player who scored against England in the 1988 European Championship finals?

38. In which year did England first play a match under the Wembley floodlights?

39. During the 1984 World Cup qualifier against Turkey, who became the first England captain to hit a hat-trick since Viv Woodward in 1909?

40. Who did Alf Ramsey succeed as England manager?

41. Striker Mark Hateley has been capped by England while on the books of four different clubs. Can you name them?

42. Which country prevented England from qualifying for the 1984 European Championship?

43. Who is the youngest man to have skippered the full England side?

44. Can you name the San Marino goalkeeper who denied David Platt a record-equalling fifth goal, by saving his penalty in the World Cup qualifier of February 1993?

45. Who was a member of both the 1982 and 1986 England World Cup squads but didn't play in either tournament?

46. What do England internationals John Barnes, Terry Butcher and Tony Dorigo have in common?

47. Against which country did full-back Lee Dixon fire home his first-ever international goal at Wembley in March 1991?

48. Which former English international goalkeeper later became Scotland's goalkeeping coach?

49. Who were the two unfortunate players who missed penalties in the shoot-out to decide the 1990 World Cup semi-final?

50. Prior to the 1988 European Champions, the England side flexed their muscles by taking on the Southern League champions Aylesbury. What was the result of the match?

51. Can you name the Manchester City striker who made his England debut against Spain in September 1992?

52. Whose goal ended England's reign as World Champions in June 1970?

53. In May 1976, which player, with 21 caps, pulled out of the England squad and asked not to be selected again?

54. England took two goalkeepers to the 1992 European Championships in Sweden. Chris Woods was one – who was the other?

55. Who was the Scotland schoolboy internationalist who went on to gain eight full caps for England between 1959 and 1966?

56. How many times have England played in the semi-finals of the World Cup?

57. Two players scored their first goal for England in a 1992 friendly against Czechoslovakia in Prague. Name either of them.

58. At which Premier League ground is the Crompton Suite, named after Bob Crompton, the famous England full-back and captain of the pre-World War One period?

59. Who is the only man to have captained and managed England?

60. Gary Pallister won his first England cap while a Second Division player – at which club?

How you fared...

46–60	Cap that!
31–45	A seasoned internationalist
16–30	More suited to club football
0–15	One-cap wonder

7
CUP CRAZY

'The beauty of the FA Cup is that the big boys can get drawn
away to any of the smaller teams with the chance that they'll get
turned over. The pitches can be a great leveller and several
times we were lucky to survive visits to places such as
York and Swansea.'

1. Who in 1993, became the first American international to play in an FA Cup Final?

2. Which was the last team to reach the FA Cup Final two years running?

3. True or false – the League Cup Final has been played at Wembley since 1965?

4. Which club won five of the first seven FA Cup Finals?

5. Which Arsenal player was booked for the first time in his career during the 1993 FA Cup Final replay?

6. How did Peter Willis make FA Cup history in 1985?

7. Name the Fourth Division side which reached the League Cup Final in 1962?

8. Who scored in the 1986 FA Cup Final but missed a penalty in the 1991 match?

9. Which team lifted the FA Cup three times during the 1950s?

10. Malcolm Shotton captained which League Cup winning side of the mid 1980s?

11. Which team has won more FA Cup ties than any other in the last ten seasons?

12. Brighton's Gordon Smith had an infamous last-minute miss in the 1983 FA Cup Final. Who was the Manchester United goalkeeper who saved his shot?

13. Which Liverpool youngster was voted 'Man of the Match' in the 1992 FA Cup Final against Sunderland?

14. Who were the first Third Division side ever to contest a Wembley Final?

15. Which First Division side's 4–1 away victory at Watford in January 1993 secured their passage to the FA Cup fourth round for the first time in ten years?

16. Can you name either of the Leeds United players from whom Sunderland's Jim Montgomery made his incredible 'double save' in the Rokerites' memorable 1973 FA Cup Final victory?

17. Which relegated team reached the Coca-Cola Cup semi-finals in 1993?

18. Who scored the only goal of the 1985 Everton–Manchester United FA Cup Final?

19. After Wembley, which other two grounds have been used most often for FA Cup Finals?

20. Which midfielder played in four League Cup Finals between 1988 and 1993?

21. Which Third Division team sent Crystal Palace crashing out of the 1993 FA Cup?

22. Between 1971 and 1980, Northern Ireland international Pat Rice appeared in five FA Cup Finals for Arsenal. How many times did he win?

23. Why was the 1993 Coca-Cola Cup Final a day of mixed emotions for Arsenal youngster Steve Morrow?

24. Which team did Graham Williams skipper to FA Cup victory during the 1960s?

25. Which Second Division side stunned Liverpool by winning 2–0 in a 1993 third round replay at Anfield?

26. Which current television expert headed Wolves' winning goal in the 1980 League Cup Final?

27. Who knocked eventual Premier League Champions Manchester United out of the 1993 FA Cup?

28. In 1971, Eddie Kelly became the first substitute to score in an FA Cup Final. Name the player who was originally credited with the goal.

29. Which First Division side were trounced 7–1 by Sheffield Wednesday in the third round of the 1992–93 Coca-Cola Cup?

30. Who is the youngest player ever to score in a League Cup Final?

31. Which defender-turned-striker was Sheffield Wednesday's leading goalscorer in their 1993 FA Cup campaign?

32. Who was the last player to score in every round of the FA Cup?

33. Where did Manchester United goalkeeper Ray Wood play during the second half of the 1957 FA Cup Final?

34. Where was a 1993 FA Cup quarter-final tie held up for 13 minutes due to a pitch invasion?

35. Name the Northern League side which took Wrexham to a fifth round FA Cup replay in 1978.

36. Why were Peterborough ordered to replay their 1992 FA Cup second round replay against Kingstonian – a match which they won 9–1?

37. Who was the first player to score in two FA Cup Finals with different clubs?

38. At the end of the 1989 Littlewoods Cup Final, who caused a storm by leaving the arena before the trophy was presented?

39. The 1970 FA Cup Final replay attracted the highest-ever British television audience for a club match. Who were the teams involved?

40. Who appeared in 88 FA Cup ties between 1962 and 1980 during his career with Liverpool, Swansea and Crewe?

41. Chris Woods has played in League Cup Finals for three different clubs. Sheffield Wednesday is one – name the other two.

42. Crystal Palace exited from the FA Cup at the third round stage in five of the six seasons from 1988 to 1993. How far did the Eagles progress in the year they made it past the third round?

43. Who were the last amateur winners of the FA Cup?

44. Can you name the brothers who played in Newcastle's FA Cup winning side of 1952?

45. Which is the only surviving club to have won the FA Cup three years in succession?

46. Which team won the FA Cup twice during the 1970s?

47. What have Stuart McCall, Alan Pardew, Dale Gordon, Dwight Yorke, John McGinlay and Andy Walker all done in various FA Cup competitions since 1989?

48. Who was Ipswich Town manager when they won the FA Cup in 1978?

49. Has any player ever been ordered off in a League Cup Final at Wembley?

50. What new FA Cup record did Bryan Robson create in May 1990?

51. Against which team did Kevin Keegan score two FA Cup Final goals?

52. Which two teams have lifted the League Cup on a record four occasions each?

53. The referee of the 1934 FA Cup Final later became the President of FIFA. Can you name him?

54. When did two London sides last contest the FA Cup Final?

55. Yeovil Town sensationally defeated Sunderland 2–1 in the fourth round of the 1949 FA Cup. What was the result of their next round tie against Manchester United?

56. Who scored in both the Coca-Cola and FA Cup Finals in 1993?

57. True or false – since 1908, the FA Cup winners have always contested the following season's Charity Shield match?

58. What, literally, cast a shadow over Wembley on FA Cup Final day in 1930?

59. In 1972, which team became the first to qualify for European football solely on the basis of winning the League Cup?

60. How many of the last ten FA Cup Finals (1984 to 1993) have gone to extra-time?

How you fared...	
46–60	Absolutely knockout!
31–45	A good cup run
16–30	Replay required
0–15	Early casualties

<u>8</u>
<u>SUPER</u>
<u>STOPPERS</u>

*'Of the current crop of English defenders, I like Tony Adams.
He's a whole-hearted player and has a lot more ability than
people give him credit for. On the world scene, I rate the
German defenders highly – their man-markers are always solid
and they stick to their system rigidly.'*

1. Which member of Denmark's 1992 European Championship winning defence signed for Liverpool in September that year?

2. True or false – Tony Adams has a full set of English domestic medals?

3. Until the end of the 1992–93 season, which defender was English football's longest-serving one-club player?

4. In 1970, which Briton was described by Pele as 'the finest defender in the world'?

5. Name the Blackburn Rovers stopper who made his Scotland debut in the World Cup qualifier in Estonia in May 1993.

6. This centre-half played in three Wembley finals with Luton and one with Brighton in the space of six years during the 1980s. Can you name him?

7. Which country did QPR centre-back Alan McDonald captain in their 1994 World Cup qualifying campaign?

8. Jack Charlton made an amazing 629 League appearances for which club between 1952 and 1972?

9. 'Killer' won an FA Cup medal in 1987 and was part of the Newcastle squad which stormed into the Premier League in 1993. Who is he?

10. Which Republic of Ireland defender was voted the PFA Player of the Year for 1992–93?

11. From which club did Liverpool sign no-nonsense centre-half Neil Ruddock?

12. Name the central defensive pairing which helped Leeds win the title in 1991–92.

13. Which defender's clubs include Aston Villa, Celtic, Luton Town and Pisa?

14. Who headed an unfortunate own goal in the 1991 FA Cup Final?

15. Name the Coventry City, Arsenal and Leicester City defender who made his one and only full international appearance for England against Yugoslavia in October 1972.

16. What does defender Eric Young wear which makes him instantly identifiable?

17. Which Manchester United centre–back missed a penalty in The Reds' 1993 FA Cup defeat at Sheffield United?

18. The £250,000 transfer barrier was broken when which defender moved from Leicester to Derby in August 1972?

19. From which club did Southampton sign Dutchman Ken Monkou in August 1992?

20. Name the iron-man defender who appeared for Liverpool in the Final of all three major European tournaments.

21. Which Northern Ireland international defender made 39 Premier League appearances for Chelsea during 92–93?

22. Which club did former Liverpool star Mark Lawrenson manage during 1988?

23. Can you name the German-born stopper who played in League Cup Finals for both Wolves and Sunderland between 1980 and 1985?

24. Which Oldham defender played against England in the 1994 World Cup qualifying competition?

25. Gary O'Reilly opened the scoring in which recent FA Cup Final?

26. Emlyn Hughes won a League Cup winners medal with which club?

27. Name the stylish sweeper who is still the only man to have captained Scottish and FA Cup winning teams.

28. Belgian-born full-back Pat Van Den Hauwe is an international cap for which country?

29. In the 1940s and '50s, which Scottish side had a strong defence nicknamed the 'Iron Curtain'?

30. Which defender headed Arsenal's late winner in the 1993 FA Cup Final replay?

31. Who was the Everton centre-half who partnered Bobby Moore in three of England's four 1970 World Cup matches?

32. From which Swedish club did Blackburn sign Patrik Andersson in January 1993?

33. Two former Liverpool defenders each made 40 appearances for Everton in the 1992–93 Premier League. Can you name either of them?

34. 'Norman Bites Yer Legs!' boasted Leeds fans during the 1970s. Who were they referring to?

35. Who was the highest-scoring defender in the 1990 World Cup tournament?

36. At which club was Mark Wright first capped?

37. Who wore the No.5 jersey in Manchester United's European Cup winning side of 1968?

38. In which year did David O'Leary make his Football League debut?

39. Which veteran West Ham defender did Trevor Brooking call his 'minder' when he played alongside him in midfield?

40. In 1973, David Webb, formerly of Chelsea, and ex-Arsenal skipper Frank McLintock linked up to form the central defensive partnership at which other London club?

41. True or false – Terry Butcher won a full set of Scottish domestic medals during his four years at Rangers?

42. Name the Welsh international defender who converted the penalty which sealed Swindon's promotion to the Premier League in May 1993.

43. For which Spanish club did Kevin Moran once play?

44. How many goals did Chris Nicholl score in Aston Villa's 2–2 draw with Leicester in 1976?

45. Who is the former Manchester City defender who helped West Bromwich Albion win the 1993 Second Division play-offs?

46. Which famous England defender has twice been the subject of 'This is Your Life' – in 1961 and 1989?

47. Who was the full-back who fired home the goal which won the 1981 European Cup for Liverpool?

48. Name the two Scots who played at the heart of Aston Villa's Championship-winning defence in 1980–81.

49. Who wore the No.5 jersey for England in the 1993 US Cup tournament?

50. How many times did Steve Perryman captain Spurs to FA Cup success?

51. Which Nottingham Forest centre-back was the Football Writers' Footballer of the Year in 1978?

52. In a 1988 friendly international at Wembley, Arsenal's Tony Adams scored for both sides. Who were England's opponents?

53. Can you name the Stoke and England centre-half who caused a sensation in 1950 by quitting English football to play in a pirate league in Colombia?

54. Which defender skippered Liverpool's League Cup winning sides of 1981 and 1982?

55. After scoring with two penalties, a defender topped England's scoring list in the 1962 World Cup finals in Chile. Can you name him?

56. What was Shaun Teale's first League club?

57. Name the centre-half who managed Spurs, Arsenal and Northern Ireland between 1971 and 1983.

58. Who was the last defender to be voted European Footballer of the Year?

59. In which year did Gary Mabbutt make his League debut – 1978, 1980 or 1982?

60. Which long-serving centre-back captained Manchester City's League Cup winning side of 1976?

How you fared...

46–60	Solid as a rock
31–45	Sound defence
16–30	A bit wobbly at the back
0–15	Leaking like a sieve

9
ALL CHANGE

'Nowadays, too many players are moving on before they've seen out their contract. That seriously affects continuity and makes it difficult to build a settled team. You can always bring in two, or maybe three players without upsetting a side, but when you get to five or six then you're in trouble.'

1. Who went in the opposite direction when Kevin Gallacher moved from Coventry to Blackburn Rovers in March 1993?

2. What transfer record was broken by the move of David Mills from Middlesbrough to West Bromwich Albion in 1979?

3. How long did Trevor Steven spend at Marseille before returning to Rangers?

4. Between September 1988 and August 1992, Wimbledon sold three players to Manchester City. Can you name them?

5. Which club did Steve Nicol leave to join Liverpool in 1981?

6. In which month is the deadline for transfers in English football?

7. Garry Parker left which club to join Aston Villa in 1991?

8. Who moved from Portsmouth to Tottenham for £2 million in the summer of 1992?

9. From which club did Chelsea sign goalkeeper Dmitri Kharin in November 1992?

10. What age was Clive Allen when he re-located from QPR to Arsenal for £1.25 million in June 1980?

11. Irish side Cobh Ramblers have, in recent seasons, sold two brothers to Nottingham Forest and Cambridge respectively. Can you name them?

12. Who said of Paul Gascoigne's move from Tottenham to Lazio: 'It's like watching your mother-in-law drive over the cliff in your new car'?

13. Who in 1928, became the first player to be sold for the then-princely sum of £10,000?

14. Which former England international defender left Everton in April 1993 – just seven weeks after joining them from Coventry?

15. In which country did England and former Spurs star Glenn Hoddle play from 1987 to 1991?

16. Who joined Arsenal from Cremonese in 1990?

17. How much did Blackburn Rovers pay Southampton to secure the services of Alan Shearer?

18. Who was the first British manager to fork out £1 million for a player?

19. Which member of Manchester United's 1993 Championship winning team cost them the most money?

20. Who appeared three times at Wembley for his new club during 1977–78 – his first season in English football?

21. How long passed between the first £1/2 million and £1 million transfers in British football – five weeks, five months or five years?

22. The 1987 Danish Player of the Year became his country's most expensive export in 1992 when he moved to an FA Premier League club. Who is he?

23. Who moved from Morton to Leeds United in 1970?

24. Can you name three former Spurs team-mates who played together at Glasgow Rangers during 1987–88?

25. In 1979, Manchester City paid Wolves £1.4 million for Steve Daley. Almost immediately Wolves spent the money on the purchase of which striker?

26. What was remarkable about the exchange transfer of two goalkeepers between QPR and Sheffield Wednesday in 1967?

27. In August 1987, Inter Milan bid £1.3 million for a Glasgow-born midfielder of Oxford United. Who is he?

28. With which club did striker Teddy Sheringham win a Second Division Championship medal in 1988?

29. Since 1980, two England internationals have moved from Nottingham Forest to Manchester United and then back again. Can you name them?

30. Allan Clarke was twice the subject of a British transfer record during the late 1960s. Which club did he eventually win a Championship medal with?

31. For which club have Robert Fleck, Andy Linighan and Andy Townsend all played?

32. Who joined Liverpool from Middlesbrough for £352,000 in January 1978?

33. Why were St Mirren pleased when Rangers' Ian Ferguson played for Scotland against Estonia in June 1993?

34. From which Northern League side did Newcastle sign Chris Waddle in 1980?

35. Which Irish international striker was once traded for 12 tracksuits and a piece of corrugated iron?

36. Name two of the clubs Peter Reid played for before he joined Manchester City.

37. When England World Cup hero Martin Peters joined Spurs in 1970, he became Britain's first £200,000 player. But do you know who moved from White Hart Lane to West Ham as part of the deal?

38. In May 1990, Arsenal laid out a record fee for a goalkeeper when they bought David Seaman. How much did they pay Queen's Park Rangers?

39. Who joined Nottingham Forest from Leeds in August 1989 but didn't play a single League match for them before moving on to Sheffield Wednesday three months later?

40. By the end of the 1991–92 season, Clive Allen had been on the books of how many different London clubs?

41. Who moved from Bournemouth to Norwich in March 1993 for £700,000 – the biggest fee on transfer deadline day?

42. Alfredo di Stefano played international football for three countries – Argentina, Spain and which other?

43. Approximately how much did Premier League clubs spend on transfer fees between March 1992 and March 1993 – £34 million, £44 million or £54 million?

44. Which Premier League club took in the most money from transfer deals during that same period?

45. Which striker became Britain's costliest player when he moved from West Ham to Everton for £2.2 million in July 1988?

46. Who left Charlton for Sampdoria in July 1955?

47. Welsh international Bryn Jones was the subject of the highest pre-war transfer fee when he moved from Wolves to which London club?

48. Who moved from Sunderland to Crystal Palace for £1.8 million in September 1991?

49. Whose list of clubs includes Paris Saint-Germain, Manchester United and Chelsea?

50. How much did Newcastle pay Everton for Peter Beardsley in June 1993?

51. At which club did Kenny Sansom begin his career?

52. Who became the first £1 million British player to be given a free transfer when he was released by Real Madrid in 1984?

53. What part did Alf Common play in transfer history?

54. Which Irish international striker had a short spell at Ajax Amsterdam during 1987–88?

55. Who was the first uncapped player to be transferred for more than £1 million?

56. Name the two brothers who moved from Southampton to Leeds in a joint deal in July 1991.

57. Owen Archdeacon, Chris Morris and Andy Walker have all moved south from which Scottish club in recent seasons?

58. Who was the most expensive foreign import playing in British football during 1992–93?

59. True or false – Kevin Keegan was the first British player to be transferred for £500,000?

60. Approximately how much did Marseille lose on Chris Waddle when they sold him to Sheffield Wednesday in June 1992?

How you fared...

46–60	Megabucks man!
31–45	A worthwhile investment
16–30	Bargain basement buy
0–15	Free transfer

10
FOOTBALL ITALIA

'Some of the Italian games are great, but if you get a bad one it can be 90 minutes of purgatory! I once watched Genoa play Milan and it was so obvious that neither side wanted to win. What you can't dispute is the high level of technical skill in the Serie A.'

1. Who were the 1993 champions of Italy?

2. On which day of the week do the Italians usually play their football?

3. Walter Zenga has kept goal in more than 300 matches for which leading Italian club?

4. Which television company was the first to screen 'live' Italian League matches in the UK?

5. Who headed Lazio's equalizer in the Rome derby match of November 1992?

6. In what way does the Italian Cup Final differ from the English and Scottish Cup Finals?

7. What are the Christian names of the two players called Baggio who starred for Juventus during '92–93?

8. Which city is home to Fiorentina?

9. Which teams contested the Final of the 1993 *Coppa Italia*?

10. Name three Aston Villa players who went on to join Bari?

11. Which then *Serie B* team defeated Derby 3–1 at Wembley to win the 1993 Anglo–Italian Cup?

12. What do Inter Milan, Atalanta and Pisa have in common?

13. Which then Lazio forward scored a winning goal against Scotland in March 1993?

14. What in Italy, is the much-sought-after *scudetto*?

15. Which current Italian international striker has winners' medals from the European Cup-Winners' Cup and UEFA Cup but only a runners-up medal from the European Cup?

16. Name the *Serie A* club based on the island of Sardinia.

17. What do the Italians call their national side?

18. In 1992, Sven Goran Eriksson replaced Vujadin Boskov as coach at which club?

19. Who topped the 1993 *Serie A* goal charts?

20. Who was the oldest player in Milan's championship winning side of 1992–93?

21. In which year did Juventus last win the Italian *Serie A*?

22. Where did David Platt's Sampdoria begin their 1993–94 championship campaign with a 2–1 away victory?

23. What is the name of Bergamo's *Serie A* side?

24. Italian striker Paolo Rossi was the top goalscorer in the 1982 World Cup. Which club was he with at that time?

25. How many Italian League championships have Lazio won?

26. Which two former Bayern Munich stars played together for Fiorentina in the 1992–93 *Serie A*?

27. In which district of Milan is the magnificent Giuseppe Meazza Stadium?

28. Who was the Torino hard-man linked, rather speculatively, with a move to Manchester City during 1992–93?

29. Which shirt number do Italian clubs usually reserve for their star player?

30. In which year were Genoa founded? (Clue: It's in the official name of the club)

31. Who, with 35 goals, is the Italian national team's leading goalscorer of all time?

32. Who did Fabio Capello succeed as Milan coach at the end of the 1990–91 season?

33. What is Italian football's ruling body known as?

34. What record did Parma's Colombian international Faustino Asprilla end in March 1993?

35. In May 1993, Sampdoria's international goalkeeper was involved in a serious car crash. Can you name him?

36. In Italy, what kind of player is a *centrocampista*?

37. Since 1990, Roma have been deprived of the services of two strikers due to suspensions on drug-related offences. Can you name the players involved?

38. In March 1993, full-back Sergio Porrini became which club's first Italian internationalist in over 30 years?

39. What was the result of both the Milan derby matches in the 1992–93 season?

40. For which Italian League club did Graeme Souness and Liam Brady both play?

41. In May 1993, what accessory did Gazza wear on his Lazio come-back after he had been injured while playing for England?

42. Which Italian club lost a great championship-winning side in a tragic air crash of 1949?

43. Name the former international goalkeeper who has coached both Juventus and Lazio.

44. Which team plays in the San Paolo Stadium?

45. The legendary Helenio Herrera was the Italian Championship and European Cup-winning coach of which club during the 1960s?

46. Romania's international skipper played for Brescia in the '92–93 *Serie A* – who is he?

47. Can you name any two of the three players on Milan's books during 1992–93 who were neither Italian nor Dutch?

48. Which two Italian clubs have won the World Club Championship?

49. Which team defeated Foggia 6–2 on the last day of the 1992–93 season but were still relegated because of the outcome of other matches?

50. Why do both Genoa and Milan use the English spelling of their cities' names as opposed to the Italian versions – Genova and Milano?

51. Name the German international christened *Tomasino* or 'Little Thomas' by AS Roma fans.

52. Which team achieved a 40-game unbeaten run between 1955 and 1956 – a record only overtaken in 1992–93 by Milan?

53. True or false – Roberto Mancini was a £2 million player as a teenager?

54. Costa Rican international Hernan Medford was on the books of which *Serie A* club during 1992–93?

55. In October 1992, which Italian defender U-turned on his decision to retire from international football?

56. Why did Fiorentina change the style of their 'away' jerseys mid-way through the 1992–93 season?

57. Name the Brazilian World Cup star who inspired Roma to the 1983 *Serie A* Championship.

58. Which of Channel Four's 'live' Italian League fixtures drew the largest TV audience during 1992–93?

59. Who was the last player from the British Isles to win an Italian Championship medal?

60. What was remarkable about the hat-trick scored by Roma's Giannini in the second leg of the 1993 Italian Cup Final?

How you fared...

46–60	Bellissimo!
31–45	Clued-up on *calcio*
16–30	You need to up the tempo
0–15	It's *Serie B* for you!

11
LAWS OF THE GAME

'The biggest recent change in the Laws of the Game is the
back-pass law and it's one I don't entirely agree with – I think it
penalizes good defending. While I can see how it adds to the
excitement, the rule makes defenders edgy and discourages good
build-up play.'

1. True or false – at a penalty-kick, the goalkeeper must stand on his goal-line, half-way between either goal-post?

2. Could a goal be scored from a wind-assisted goal-kick?

3. What is the punishment for dangerous play?

4. What does the referee indicate by showing the yellow, then the red card to a player?

5. True or false – once the referee has signalled for a free-kick to be taken, opposing players can move towards the ball?

6. Can a goalkeeper swap places with a team-mate during a match?

7. How high above the ground should the crossbars be?

8. At a indirect free-kick, an attacking player taps the ball 12 inches to a team-mate who sweeps it into the net. Should the referee award a goal?

9. True or false – a throw-in taken from the wrong place must be re-taken?

10. Should a referee send off a player for dissent?

11. Why did most goalkeepers in the inaugural Premier League not wear green jerseys?

12. When a penalty shoot-out is required, what is the first decision that the referee must make?

13. True or false – shirt-pulling should be penalised by an indirect free-kick?

14. In 1992, what change was made to the Law regarding taking of goal-kicks?

15. Can a player be sent off for wearing dangerously long studs on his boots?

16. What relevance does '0.6–1.1 atmospheres' have to the Laws of the Game?

17. While waiting for a corner-kick to be taken, a defender punches an attacker in the penalty-box. What action should the referee take?

18. Which is the only penalty offence which does not involve a physical act against an opponent?

19. Can a referee ever alter his decision?

20. When is an orange-coloured ball sometimes used?

21. Can a game continue if four players of one side have been ordered off?

22. Should a player wearing a plaster be allowed to compete in a match?

23. If a referee orders a penalty kick to be re-taken, can another player take the kick?

24. True or false – the goal-posts must be round?

25. What is the size of the goal-area, in square yards?

26. Is it permissible for one team to play in sky blue shirts and the other in royal blue?

27. After a goalkeeper has saved a penalty-kick, the referee notices that a defender is standing by the corner-flag. What action should he take?

28. May a player who is taking a penalty attempt to deceive the opposing goalkeeper as to where he is going to place the ball?

29. True or false – a soccer pitch is always larger than an American Football field?

30. What action should a referee take if he notices a player is bleeding from a head cut?

31. Can a substitute come on specifically to take a penalty?

32. At a penalty-kick, the ball is stopped from entering the goal by a spectator. Should the referee award a goal or a drop-ball?

33. True or false – in a penalty shoot-out, all players except the goalkeepers are eligible to take kicks?

34. What should be awarded when an attacker strikes an indirect free-kick directly into goal?

35. Can a team wear an all-yellow strip in the first-half of a match and then change into a red kit for the second half?

36. Should a referee send off a goalkeeper for handling outside of his penalty-area?

37. Could a goal ever be allowed from a throw?

38. May a player take two kicks during a penalty shoot-out?

39. Can a referee insist on starting the second half immediately the first half has ended?

40. Is it possible for a team to kick-off three times in succession, without a goal being scored between any of the kick-offs?

41. Can an attacking team ever take an indirect free-kick one yard from their opponent's goal?

42. Should a goal be awarded if a goalkeeper strikes a goal-kick against the referee and the ball rebounds from him back into the net?

43. Which part of a football pitch comprises an area of approximately 314 square yards?

44. If a defender handles the ball on the line of the penalty-area, what should the referee award?

45. May a team play in a match wearing track-suit trousers?

46. Should the game continue if the ball rebounds from the corner-flag or half-way flag?

47. Which item of players' equipment was made compulsory by FIFA in 1990?

48. True or false – a team can win a penalty shoot-out by taking only three kicks?

49. What term is often used to describe the illegal and intentional denial of a clear goalscoring opportunity by a defending player?

50. True or false – the new Law of 1992 made all back-passes illegal?

51. From a long throw-in, the ball sails high into the penalty-area and the goalkeeper accidentally punches it into his own net. Is it a goal?

52. How does the referee re-start the game after he has ordered off a player for using foul and abusive language?

53. How was the offside law changed in 1990?

54. Is it ever permissible to charge an opponent from behind?

55. What is the maximum length of a football pitch which is used for international matches?

56. True or false – the referee should blow for time-wasting if a goalkeeper holds onto the ball for more than four seconds?

57. Can the ball ever be allowed to weigh more than 16 ounces?

58. Is it permissible for a player to shout: 'My ball!'?

59. What is the minimum height which a corner-flag must be?

60. If an attacker, in an offside position, steps over the bye-line to indicate that he is not interfering with play, should he be penalized?

How you fared...

46–60	Eagle-eyed whistler
31–45	Competent official
16–30	Consult your linesman more
0–15	Who's the $*£%@& in the black?

12
SCOTTISH
FOOTBALL

'For me, the only way to gauge the strength of
a country's football is by how many teams it has left in Europe
come March. In that respect, Scotland has fared badly for
quite a while now. However, I was very impressed with the
performances of Rangers in the 1992–93
Champions League.'

1. Which team were runners-up to Rangers in the 1992–93 Scottish Premier League, Skol Cup and Scottish Cup?

2. Name the veteran Dundee United manager who finally decided to retire in May 1993.

3. Who are still referred to as 'The Lisbon Lions'?

4. What are the colours of Hearts?

5. For which team did Andy Gray play in the Scottish Cup Final of 1974?

6. Which former Motherwell player scored a European Cup goal against Rangers in 1992?

7. How many Glasgow-based teams played in the 1957–58 Scottish First Division?

8. Can you name the former FA Cup winning captain who played briefly for Dundee during 1992–93?

9. At which club was defender Davie McPherson first capped?

10. Which Scottish side are nicknamed 'The Warriors'?

11. Which member of Rangers' 1991–92 League-winning squad had previously won championship medals in two other countries?

12. In which year did Paul McStay first play for Scotland?

13. Name the beaten semi-finalists in the 1993 Scottish Cup.

14. Which Rangers player scored against Celtic at least once in every season from 1983 to 1992?

15. Which former Manchester United and Northern Ireland star guided Raith Rovers into the Premier League in 1992–93?

16. How did the name CR Smith connect Celtic and Rangers from 1984 to 1987?

17. Which Premier League manager was ordered off in a 1993 Scottish Cup tie against Dumbarton?

18. Which club has supplied the more full Scottish internationals – Hearts or Hibs?

19. Name the former UEFA Cup winner who kept goal for Falkirk during 1992–93.

20. Can you list the three Scottish clubs whose name includes a point of the compass?

21. Fans of which Second Division club formed a 'bearded army' in honour of their team's manager, Danny McGrain?

22. 'The Lawman' Denis Law scored 30 goals for his country but did he ever play in Scottish football?

23. Which is the only 1993–94 Premier League club never to have appeared in European competition?

24. Can you name the two members of Rangers' 'M & B' striking partnership of the early 1960s?

25. Why were Elgin City stripped of their Highland League title in 1993?

26. The late, great Jock Stein turned out for two Scottish clubs as a player – can you name them?

27. What is the unusual feature of Airdrie's jersey?

28. Who moved from West Ham to Celtic for £1.5 million in August 1992?

29. Can you name the two former Falkirk striking partners who went on to manage Scotland?

30. Who was the 1993 Scottish Footballer of the Year?

31. Name two of Fife's four Scottish League clubs.

32. Which Hamilton Accies star played against Scotland in May 1992?

33. Darren Jackson was which club's leading scorer for the 1992–93 season?

34. Which club has qualified more often for European competition – Aberdeen or Dundee United?

35. Who was the first Scotland player to be ordered off during Andy Roxburgh's reign as international manager?

36. Which team was known as Ferranti Thistle until they joined the Scottish League in 1974?

37. In 1992, Ally McCoist became the first Briton since Ian Rush to win which prestigious goalscoring award?

38. With which club did John Collins make his Premier League debut in 1985?

39. Which team have lost the Scottish Championship title on both goal average and goal difference since 1965?

40. Derek Johnstone scored over 200 goals in 500-plus games for Rangers. But for which other club did he play Premier League football in October 1983?

41. Which club traditionally sold themselves to prospective fans on the catchphrase 'Firhill for Thrills'?

42. Which clubs met each other in four Skol Cup Finals between 1987 and 1992?

43. Who succeeded Billy McNeill as Celtic manager in 1983?

44. One of the first £1 million pound signings in British football, this striker failed to save Airdrie from relegation in the 1992–93 season. Who is he?

45. From whom did Aberdeen sign goalkeeper Theo Snelders?

46. How many clubs played in the old-style Scottish First Division prior to League reconstruction in 1975?

47. Which former Celtic team-mates steered Kilmarnock to promotion in 1993?

48. True or false – Graeme Souness was Rangers' first-ever player–manager?

49. BBC presenter John Leslie is an avid fan of which Scottish Premier League side?

50. Who is the Scottish Football correspondent for BBC Radio's *Sport on 5*?

51. Who replaced Joe Jordan as Hearts manager in May 1993?

52. What is the smallest place in Scotland with a Scottish League team?

53. Name the youngster who opened the scoring for Rangers in the 1993 Scottish Cup Final.

54. What is St Mirren's best-ever finishing position in the Scottish Premier League?

55. In 1992–93, full-back Fraser Wishart suffered the trauma of relegation for the second successive season. Can you name either of the teams he was involved with?

56. Which 1960s star was known as 'The Wee Prime Minister'?

57. Which team drew the lowest average crowd during 1992–93 – Albion Rovers, Berwick Rangers or Stenhousemuir?

58. How many different clubs have won the Scottish Premier League?

59. At which club did Gordon Strachan begin his career?

60. Which Premier League captain was born in Stockholm?

How you fared...

46–60	Mac-nificent!
31–45	Fairly Jock-wise
16–30	Take the Low Road!
0–15	You must be English!

13
FACTS AND
FEATS

'We broke quite a few records at Liverpool but never thought about them at the time. It's only when you look back years later that you might think 'that was good' or whatever. One of the great strengths of the management at Anfield was that they never allowed you to believe you were doing well.'

1. Who was the first man to win successive English Championship medals with two different clubs?

2. Which First Division side went 42 League matches undefeated between November 1977 and December 1978?

3. Matt Busby lead Manchester United to how many First Division titles between 1946 and 1971?

4. Clive Allen netted a tournament-record twelve goals for which club in the 1986–87 League Cup?

5. Who holds the record for being the old First Division's youngest scorer?

6. Which was the first British team to win a major European trophy in addition to a domestic League and Cup double?

7. In 1961, England chalked up their highest-ever win over Scotland. What was the score?

8. How many goals did Bournemouth's Ted MacDougall score against Margate in the 1971 FA Cup?

9. Goalkeeper Chris Woods kept a clean sheet for 1,196 minutes during 1986–87. Which club was he with at that time?

10. Which team ended Newcastle's club record eleven-match unbeaten start to the 1992–93 First Division season?

11. Who re-wrote the First Division record books when he netted seven times for Arsenal against Aston Villa in 1935?

12. How many League titles did Leeds win under Don Revie?

13. Which Scottish club failed to win a single League match at home during 1992–93?

14. Which team has made the most FA Cup Final appearances?

15. In 1983, who made history by becoming the first manager to be presented with a major trophy at Wembley?

16. Which is the only team to have scored and conceded 100 or more goals in a single Football League season?

17. What unenviable record did Jose Batista set in 1986?

18. Who scored four times in a 1989 European Cup-Winners' Cup tie yet still finished on the losing side?

19. Which English club has had the most post-war managers?

20. Who appeared in eight championship-winning teams for Liverpool between 1975 and 1985?

21. What Football League record does Arthur Rowley hold?

22. Which country went a record 29 internationals undefeated until they lost to West Germany in the 1954 World Cup Final?

23. Which was the first English club to gain 100 points in a season?

24. Which Portuguese club holds the record for the biggest win in any European tie?

25. Which was the first team to win the League Championship without losing a match?

26. Who was reputedly the first British footballer to be paid £100-a-week?

27. Who is the youngest manager to take a team to the FA Cup Final at Wembley?

28. Which team has won the League of Ireland Championship on the most occasions?

29. How many hat-tricks did Dixie Dean hit during his career?

30. Who in 1965, became the first team to rise from the Fourth Division to the First Division of the Football League?

31. Which English club have now gone a record 80 seasons without being relegated?

32. Which two teams jointly hold the record for the longest undefeated start to a season in the old First Division?

33. Against which fellow British country did Scotland notch up their record win of 11–0?

34. Who is the oldest player ever to take part in an English First Division match?

35. The lowest post-war FA Cup semi-final crowd watched which two teams meet at White Hart Lane in 1988?

36. Morton won a record 23 successive matches in which Scottish Division during 1963–64?

37. How many different Liverpool players found the net against Crystal Palace in September 1989?

38. Which English player has made the most individual appearances at Wembley?

39. Name one of the three clubs which share the record for the most World Club Championship wins.

40. Which Liverpool striker scored in ten successive First Division matches in 1987?

41. Which is the only club to have played in the FA Premier League plus all six previous Divisions of the Football League?

42. Has an officially-registered crowd of 150,000 ever watched a football match in Britain?

43. Who was the first man to miss a penalty in a Wembley FA Cup Final?

44. What is remarkable about the 357 League goals scored by Jimmy Greaves?

45. Who in 1983, became the first Briton to appear in 1,000 first-class matches?

46. Which team holds the record for the biggest Scottish Cup Final win since World War II?

47. What age was Britain's oldest international, Billy Meredith, when he played for Wales against England in 1920?

48. What is the fewest number of players used by an English Championship winning team?

49. Which team missed three penalties in a Second Division match against Brighton in March 1989?

50. Which country's teams have won the most European club tournaments?

51. Who won the PFA Young Player of the Year award for the second successive season in 1993?

52. Which London team holds the record for the biggest win in front of the *Match of the Day* cameras?

53. What ignominious first did Hereford United achieve in their 1–1 draw at Northampton in September 1992?

54. Leeds United trounced Chelsea 7–0 in October 1967. How many different players scored?

55. Colin Clarke is which country's all-time top goalscorer?

56. What unwelcome 'first' of the 1992–93 season did Millwall's Malcolm Allen become against Watford in August?

57. Who was the last player to win successive FA Cup medals with different clubs?

58. How many times was Torquay striker Dave Caldwell ordered off during the 1987–88 season?

59. Who is the Republic of Ireland's all-time leading scorer?

60. Which striker scored a total of seven goals in the Football League play-off matches at the end of 1987–88?

How you fared...

46–60	Would you believe it?
31–45	Extremely noteworthy
16–30	Makes you go 'mmm...'
0–15	Nothing to shout about

14
STADIA STATS

'Although I can see the point of view of supporters who have stood on terraces all their life, I think the case for all-seater stadia is overwhelming. It'll be good to see, in the next ten years or so, many British grounds coming up to the level of the top continental stadia.'

1. Marlow were drawn at home to Tottenham in the third round of the 1993 FA Cup. At which ground was the match played?

2. Which Viennese stadium was renamed the 'Ernst Happel Stadion' after the late Austrian national team boss?

3. At which Premier League ground is the popular Gallowgate end?

4. Where was the 1993 Scottish Cup Final held?

5. Who scored a vital World Cup goal for Scotland on his own club ground in 1977?

6. Which was the first English League club to install an artificial playing surface in their stadium?

7. Why were Arsenal in trouble over the mural erected at Highbury in 1992?

8. Who plays at St Andrews?

9. Which of the Manchester grounds suffered bomb damage during the war?

10. The design of Rangers' Ibrox Stadium is reputedly based on which German ground?

11. Which ground housed the largest crowd of the 1992–93 English Premier League programme?

12. Which Football League club formerly played at Sophia Gardens, now the home of Glamorgan County Cricket Club?

13. What is the most northerly league ground in England?

14. At which ground do the Republic of Ireland normally play their home matches?

15. At which ground was the record attendance for a Football League match set?

16. Has European football ever been played at QPR's Loftus Road ground?

17. What major sporting event can be partly viewed from Fulham's Craven Cottage?

18. Where did Maidstone United play their Football League matches before they folded in August 1992?

19. Which team has played 'home' European competition matches at Old Trafford and Hampden Park?

20. What is the most westerly senior league ground on the British mainland?

21. Because of an enforced closure to Elland Road, Leeds United staged their first four home matches of 1971–72 at Hillsborough, Leeds Road and which other ground?

22. Which ground holds the attendance record for both the European Cup and the European Championship tournaments?

23. Which ground holds the attendance record for an FA Cup Final not held at Wembley?

24. Which British ground is closest to the sea?

25. The capacity of which London ground was slashed from 66,000 to 20,000 in 1977?

26. Which Football League ground is the furthest apart from any other?

27. Oxford United were the first and Stranraer the last – to do what at their ground?

28. Which two senior British grounds are in the same street?

29. Feyenoord fans affectionately call their stadium 'De Kuip'. What does that mean in English?

30. Where is the Racecourse Ground?

31. Which ground was flooded when the River Trent burst its banks in 1947?

32. Which other sport was played at Sheffield United's Bramall Lane until 1973?

33. In which capital city is the ground known as Parc Astrid?

34. Which team moved from The Old Show Ground to Glanford Park in 1988?

35. Which Midlands ground housed the old Second Division's record crowd in 1937?

36. In 1982–83, Rugby League club Hunslet began using which major soccer ground for their home matches?

37. Which two stadia hosted Scotland's international matches during the 1992–93 season?

38. Which Football League club plays at St James Park?

39. Which was the last English ground other than Wembley to stage a full international match?

40. What is the record crowd at an amateur match in Britain – 10,000, 50,000 or 100,000?

41. In 1993, Clyde FC planned to leave their temporary home in Hamilton to move into a new stadium in which Scottish new town?

42. In which city is the Stadion Crvena Zvezda – also known as the 'Yugo–Marakana'?

43. Which country played full international matches at Hull and Coventry during 1972–73?

44. If you were walking down Warwick Road North, to which Premier League ground would you be travelling?

45. Where in France is the ground known as *Le Stadium*?

46. In which year did Wembley first house a capacity all-seated crowd?

47. Which team plays at the 6,000-capacity Deva Stadium, Bumpers Lane?

48. What is the inscription above the Bill Shankly Gates at Liverpool's Anfield Ground?

49. In December 1992, which two teams attracted the inaugural Premier League's lowest gate?

50. What is the name of Kent's only Football League ground?

51. Which club's ground had originally been built for the Devonport Rugby Club?

52. By the end of the 1992–93 season, how many FA Cup semi-finals had been played at Wembley?

53. Who plays at Fratton Park?

54. Which was the first English ground to be visited by TV cameras?

55. Where do Coventry City play their home matches?

56. Who set up home in Exeter City's St James Park during the war?

57. Somerton Park staged League football between 1920 and 1988. Who played there?

58. In which year did Wales first play an international match at Cardiff Arms Park – 1896, 1953 or 1989?

59. Which Football League club shared Macclesfield Town's Moss Rose ground during 1991–92?

60. What happened to Celtic's famous standing enclosure 'The Jungle' in 1993?

How you fared...

46–60	Electric atmosphere
31–45	Noisy, partisan crowd
16–30	The fans are subdued
0–15	You only sing when you're winning!

15
THE
EUROPEAN
CUPS

*'I was initially dead against the new Champions League format
but I've enjoyed the matches I've seen. Teams were going away
from home and trying to win – which is great.
I don't see a full-blown European League working though –
there would be too many problems with that.'*

1. Who headed Marseille's winner in the 1993 European Cup Final against Milan?

2. Which team won the first five European Cup tournaments?

3. Name the Belgian international who played for Italian club Parma against his fellow countrymen of Antwerp in the 1993 European Cup-Winners' Cup Final.

4. Who scored in both legs of the 1992 'Battle of Britain' European Cup tie between Rangers and Leeds United?

5. Which is the only Greek club to have taken part in a major European club final?

6. Why were Leeds re-instated in the 1992–93 European Cup after losing to VfB Stuttgart on the away goals rule?

7. Which was the first British side to win a European tournament?

8. Where did Manchester United go out of the 1992–93 UEFA Cup on a penalty shoot-out?

9. Who scored all four goals for Milan against Gothenburg in the 1992–93 Champions League match at San Siro?

10. Which was the first team to lift the European Cup after a shoot-out?

11. In which country did the Russian club CSKA play their three 'home' matches in the 1992–93 Champions League?

12. Can you name the English international who played against Nottingham Forest in the 1980 European Cup Final?

13. What is the furthest that a Danish team has progressed in any European tournament?

14. Stevan Stojanovic, who kept goal for Antwerp in the 1993 Cup-Winners' Cup Final, had earlier won a Champions' Cup medal with which club in 1991?

15. In which season was Italy last unrepresented in any of the three major European tournament Finals?

16. Which team has played 'home' European competition matches at Home Park, Plymouth and Maine Road, Manchester?

17. Three German internationals won European club tournament medals in 1993. Can you name them?

18. Where was the first European Cup Final played?

19. Which Rangers striker missed the Ibrox side's crunch 1993 Champions League tie in Marseille after being ordered off against Club Bruges?

20. What feat have Alex Ferguson and Johan Cruyff both achieved in European competition?

21. In 1993, Antwerp became the fourth Belgian club to play in the European Cup-Winners' Cup Final. Can you name two of the other three?

22. Which Bayern Munich player said English football was 'stupid' after his team drew 0–0 with Liverpool at Anfield in the 1981 European Cup semi-final first leg?

23. Which Leeds-born player appeared against his home town club in the 1992–93 European Cup?

24. Which team lost in three successive European Cup semi-finals between 1988 and 1990?

25. What was the previous name of the tournament which is now the UEFA Cup?

26. Which Dutch team won the European Cup by playing 'Total Football' during the early 1970s?

27. What change did Barcelona players make before receiving their European Cup medals after defeating Sampdoria in 1992?

28. How many of the last sixteen European Cup Finals have finished with the scoreline 1–0?

29. Name the Dutchman who scored twice for Anderlecht in both the 1976 and 1978 European Cup-Winners' Cup Finals.

30. What was different about the Fairs Cup Finals of 1964 and 1965?

31. Which was the first British team to lose a European final on a penalty shoot-out?

32. What do Berne, Gothenburg, Rotterdam, Lisbon and London have in common?

33. On the two occasions Manchester United have won major European trophies, they played in a change strip. What colours did they wear?

34. Three teams from the former East Germany reached European tournament finals between 1974 and 1987. Name two of them.

35. Which two English clubs have competed in the Fairs/UEFA Cups on most occasions?

36. Which was the first British ground to stage a European club final?

37. Why were Liverpool players aggrieved about Inter Milan's free-kick goal against them in the 1965 European Cup tie in Milan?

38. Which two British sides have played in the Final of all three European tournaments?

39. To what did the headline 'Forest Sunk by Japanese Sub' refer in 1979?

40. Which German scored six goals in Inter Milan's successful UEFA Cup campaign of 1990–91?

41. Which was the first continental team to win at Anfield in European competition?

42. Which Milan superstar was subbed near the end of the 1993 European Cup Final?

43. Where did Aston Villa win the European Cup in 1982?

44. Which Leeds player had what looked like a legitimate goal disallowed in their 1975 European Cup Final defeat by Bayern Munich?

45. How many different Italian clubs have won the European Cup-Winners' Cup?

46. Marseille met two British clubs on their way to success in the 1993 European Cup. Rangers were one – who was the other?

47. Has any team ever retained the European Cup-Winners' Cup?

48. Who scored Nottingham Forest's winning goal in the 1980 Champions' Cup Final against Hamburg?

49. Which two French sides lost in the semi-finals of the 1993 UEFA Cup?

50. Can you name the German international who was twice a loser to Liverpool in Champions' Cup Finals?

51. In 1972, Wolves played in the first Final of the re-named UEFA Cup competition. Which team beat them 3–2 on aggregate?

52. Which European medal did Gary Lineker win with Barcelona?

53. True or false – as the last winners of the Fairs Cup tournament in 1971, Leeds United were allowed to keep the trophy?

54. In 1988, a Spanish side lost the UEFA Cup Final after being three goals up from the first leg. Can you name them?

55. The Liverpool team which lost to Juventus in the 1985 European Cup Final contained only two Englishmen. Can you name them?

56. Which German side knocked Sheffield Wednesday out of the 1992–93 UEFA Cup?

57. Which club won the Fairs Cup after finishing tenth in their national championship the previous season?

58. Which was the last Hungarian side to play in a European tournament final?

59. Which British player scored in both a Fairs Cup and UEFA Cup Final?

60. Britain had six representatives in European semi-finals in 1983–84. Spurs and Liverpool made it to their respective Finals. Can you name any two of the four beaten sides?

How you fared...

46–60	Kings of Europe!
31–45	Stylishly-continental
16–30	Concentrate on the domestic scene!
0–15	European chumps!

16
THE GAFFERS

*'For all the pressure there is on a player, you can multiply that by ten for a manager – he's got to answer to everybody.
I knew that when I finished playing, I would get out of the game. Management was never for me – I just didn't fancy it.'*

1. At the end of 1992–93, who replaced Brian Clough as the longest-serving one-club manager in English football?

2. Which manager led QPR to Wembley in 1982?

3. Whose successes as a manager include the 1969 and 1972 Fourth Division championships and the 1976 FA Cup?

4. Which was the first trophy won by Alex Ferguson as Manchester United boss?

5. In which year did Ron Atkinson leave Sheffield Wednesday for Aston Villa?

6. Which now-retired manager often boasts: 'I've had more clubs than Jack Nicklaus'?

7. Who in 1992, became the first foreign manager to lead an English team out at a Wembley cup final?

8. In terms of trophies won, who is Liverpool's most successful manager of all-time?

9. Who was nicknamed 'Houdini' after masterminding several relegation escapes with Charlton in the late 1980s?

10. In March 1993, Barry Fry took charge of which club after leaving his beloved Barnet?

11. Who was the manager of Spurs' 1961 Double-winning side?

12. With which club did George Graham win a League Cup medal in 1965?

13. Who is the only man to have guided a team to the Scottish Premier League and English Second Division titles?

14. Which is the only club that Bobby Robson has taken to a league championship?

15. Can you name the 65-year-old who took charge at Bristol Rovers in November 1992?

16. Whose managerial ports of call include Walsall, Swindon, Derby and Doncaster?

17. Who was the only Irishman managing an English Premier League club during 1992–93?

18. Name the last two men to lead Everton to the League Championship.

19. Who was the first England manager to fail to negotiate a World Cup qualifying tournament?

20. Ex-Aberdeen and St Mirren boss Alex Smith led which club to the 1993 Scottish Second Division Championship?

21. Who was the first man to manage Aston Villa, Birmingham and West Bromwich Albion?

22. This manager retired in 1987 having bossed each of Blackpool, Bury, Carlisle, Rochdale and, most famously, Sunderland on two separate occasions. Who is he?

23. Who was the first Englishman to manage a European Cup-winning side?

24. Name either of the teams which Ian Greaves steered to the Second Division title between 1970 and 1978.

25. In what way did QPR player–manager Trevor Francis lead by example in September 1989?

26. Who was the first manager to take Watford into the English First Division?

27. Which manager was the subject of a hit record by comedian Andy Cameron in 1978?

28. Plymouth Argyle's player–manager was ordered off for a professional foul during 1992–93. Can you name him?

29. Which club sacked Neil Warnock in January 1993?

30. Sir Stanley Matthews was general manager of which club between 1965 and 1968?

31. Name the man who managed Orient, Chelsea and Manchester United between 1965 and 1981.

32. How long was Steve Coppell in charge at Crystal Palace?

33. Can you name the controversial, former Cambridge United boss who suffered relegation with Preston North End in 1993?

34. Gerry Francis was sacked as manager of which club in 1984?

35. Which former Manchester United star was assistant to Alex Ferguson during The Reds' 1992–93 Premier League campaign?

36. Who did Mike Walker succeed as Norwich City manager?

37. Which was the first Football League club to be managed by Ron Atkinson?

38. True or false – successful manager Lou Macari is a four-times-capped Italian international?

39. Which former England defender replaced Martin Crosby as Sunderland boss during 1992–93?

40. Which club have Ron Suart, Ken Shellito and Geoff Hurst all managed?

41. Which football boss said: 'I don't drop players – I make changes'?

42. The opposing sides in the 1979 European Cup Final were both managed by Englishmen. Who were the men concerned?

43. Who bossed Wimbledon to FA Cup glory in 1988?

44. Who is the only man to have led the same club to the championships of the old-style First, Second and Third Divisions of the Football League?

45. Why did Leeds manager Don Revie change the club's strip from blue-and-gold to all-white during the 1960s?

46. Which manager signed Ossie Ardiles for Spurs and later became his assistant at West Bromwich Albion?

47. Alex Ferguson's son Darren made 15 League appearances for Manchester United during 1992–93. What connection did his other son Jason have with the Premier League?

48. Which former Scotland captain succeeded Phil Neal as Bolton Wanderers manager in May 1992?

49. Who was the only English manager in the 1992–93 Scottish Premier League?

50. Which Spanish side did Howard Kendall manage?

51. Name the Yugoslavian international who succeeded Jim McLean as Dundee United manager in 1993.

52. Who bossed Lincoln to the Fourth Division title in 1975–76?

53. Which former Leeds and Scotland star has had two spells in charge of Doncaster Rovers?

54. Which manager said in October 1991: 'I've decided to pick my moment to quit very carefully – in about 200 years time'?

55. How many League Championships did Liverpool win under Bob Paisley?

56. What title, instead of 'manager', did Andy Roxburgh's adopt when he took charge of the Scotland team in 1986?

57. Which club did Jimmy Hill manage from 1961 to 1967?

58. Name the physiotherapist who became manager of Arsenal's Double-winning side.

59. Which Championship-winning boss wrote the book 'Managing to Succeed'?

60. Who devised the board game called 'The Manager'?

How you fared...	
46–60	Wonderboss!
31–45	Very much in charge
16–30	Prone to tactical errors
0–15	Rookie coach

17
AT HOME AND ABROAD

'The Japanese are obviously trying to develop their football and they might eventually make a go of it – if they can get some players under 30! African teams like Cameroon are great to watch, but I don't think they're organized enough to win the World Cup – there's a lack of discipline about them.'

1. When did Aldershot play their last Football League match?

2. Which country won the 1992 African Nations Cup by defeating Ghana on a penalty shoot-out?

3. What colour of jerseys do Blackpool play in?

4. In which country does the team Mighty Blackpool play?

5. Which international tournament did Chesterfield win in the 1980–81 season?

6. In which part of the world is the FIFA administrative region known as CONCACAF?

7. Vauxhall Conference outfit Dagenham & Redbridge lost a thrilling local derby in the first round of the 1992–93 FA Cup. Which East London Football League club defeated them 5–4?

8. Argentinian forward Ramon Diaz won an Italian Championship medal with which club in 1989?

9. True or false – Everton have made more FA Cup semi-final appearances than any other team?

10. Which South American country has a First Division side called Everton?

11. The FGIT was set up in Britain in 1975. What do the letters FGIT stand for?

12. What world record is held by the Flamengo v Fluminense, Rio de Janeiro derby match of 1963?

13. In 1991, Gretna became the first Scottish club to appear in the FA Cup proper in105 years. Which Lancashire-based Fourth Division club ended their fairytale after a replay?

14. Which Japanese city is home to Grampus Eight?

15. What is the highest English division that Hereford United have played in?

16. Honduras drew with which British national team during the 1982 World Cup finals in Spain?

17. Andy Impey made 39 Premier League appearances for which club during 1992–93?

18. Independiente are a leading club side in which country?

19. Which is the only British League club with a 'J' in its name?

20. In June 1970, the Jalisco Stadium was the setting for one of England's most-important matches of all time. In which Mexican city is it?

21. Where do Kettering Town play their home matches?

22. Kashima Antlers made a blistering start to Japan's new J-League in May 1993. Which former Brazilian Minister of Sport grabbed a hat-trick in their 5–0 win over Grampus Eight?

23. What were Leyton Orient known as from 1966 to 1987?

24. For what unusual reason did Libya pull out of a World Cup qualifying round tie against Algeria in January 1989?

25. Which Welsh Vauxhall Conference side are nicknamed 'The Martyrs'?

26. Ladislao Mazurkiewicz was a famous World Cup goalkeeper for which South American country?

27. True or false – Notts County are the oldest club in the Football League?

28. The New Zealand national side get their nickname from the colour of their strip. What is it?

29. How many seasons did Oxford United spend in the First Division during the 1980s?

30. In which country does the team known as O'Higgins play?

31. Which English club was originally known as Pine Villa?

32. For which national team does Abedi Pele star?

33. Name the former England international midfielder who captained Queen's Park Rangers during 1992–93?

34. The Mexican city of Queretaro hosted the West Germany–Scotland tie in the 1986 World Cup. Who scored Scotland's goal in their 2–1 defeat?

35. Name either of the two Scots who have managed Reading since 1989.

36. Which city is home to Racing Club and River Plate?

37. In which League do Sutton United play?

38. True or false – Ruud Gullit was born in Surinam?

39. Which member of England's 1966 World Cup winning side later managed Telford United?

40. In which year did Brazil's Tostao win a World Cup winner's medal?

41. In August 1991, Underhill staged the first-ever Football League match of which club?

42. What is the lofty claim to fame of Peruvian club side Union Minas?

43. In which league do the side called VS Rugby play?

44. Which Rio-based club is named after a 16th Century Portuguese navigator?

45. Which uncompromising full-back moved from Wealdstone to Coventry in 1983 and went on to captain England?

46. George Weah, who has starred in France for both Monaco and Paris Saint-Germain, is an international cap for which African country?

47. Which Welsh Football League club has an 'x' in its name?

48. Daniel Xuereb is thought to be the only player, whose name begins with an 'x', to have taken part in the World Cup finals. Which country did he represent?

49. What is the distinctive feature of Yeovil's Huish ground?

50. Which African country is home to the team known as 'The Young Ones'?

51. Chris Zoricich was, alphabetically, the last player in the Football League during 1992–93. For which London team did he make 10 appearances?

52. Twice winners of the African Champions Cup, Zamalek are based in which city?

53. What is the full name of the Vauxhall Conference club from Northwich?

54. Which former World Cup winners did North Korea shock in the 1966 tournament?

55. Has the town of South Shields ever supported a team in the Football League?

56. How many matches have South Korea won in their three appearances in the World Cup finals?

57. Which Football League side formerly played at Eastville?

58. What is the name of the large stadium, situated in East Rutherford, New Jersey, which will stage seven matches in the 1994 World Cup finals?

59. What was the last major trophy won by West Bromwich Albion?

60. Did Western Samoa take part in the 1994 World Cup qualifying competition?

How you fared...

46–60	So cosmopolitan!
31–45	Far-travelled fan
16–30	A bit parochial
0–15	Stay-at-home sort

18
TRIVIA
TEASERS

*'I was never particularly into the showbiz side of
things, like pop records, but it's usual to make one if you get
to the Cup Final. The best one we did was the 'Anfield Rap'
which Craig Johnston wrote – it even reached No. 3 in
the European charts.'*

1. What part did 'Pickles' play in World Cup history?

2. Name Buckinghamshire's Football League club.

3. After Saturday, on which day of the week did Manchester United play most of their matches during '92–93?

4. Jan Ludwig Hoch was chairman of which League club from 1987 to 1991?

5. How did the Liverpool-Arsenal match of August 1964 make history?

6. In 1993, which tough-tackling midfielder made an assault on the pop charts with a re-make of the 1960s hit 'Woolly Bully'?

7. Why did the entire Celtic team wear a No.8 on their shorts in their match against Clyde of September 1973?

8. Which actor kept goal for the allied team in *Escape to Victory*?

9. Why are West Ham known as 'The Hammers'?

10. What did the Brazilian Football Confederation order referees to clamp down on, in April 1993?

11. What connection do HF Lyte and WH Monk have with the FA Cup Final?

12. Which was the first major English club to carry corporate advertising on their shirts?

13. At a towering 6ft 7ins, this Stockport County striker was the tallest player in the 1992–93 Football League. Who is he?

14. For what magnanimous gesture was German player Frank Ordenewicz awarded the 1988 FIFA Fair Play prize?

15. In March 1993, which comic book soccer hero hung up his boots after almost 40 years at the top?

16. Who did pop star Madonna vote the most handsome player of the 1990 World Cup?

17. Which 1970s player was reputedly thrown out of Gamblers' Anonymous for betting on how long he would stay in it?

18. Who told Leeds United fans in May 1992: 'I don't know why I love you – but I love you!'?

19. Leading politician Kenneth Clarke is a fan of which club?

20. What role did Berni Bunny perform in June 1992?

21. What unusual method of hooligan-control did the Bristol police adopt against Spurs fans before a Second Division match of 1977–78?

22. Who said in October 1992: 'There's only one United – Carlisle United!'

23. Alphabetically, which club follows Oxford United in the Football League?

24. Which Eastern European country blamed their 1993 World Cup qualifying defeat by Austria on a deliberately poor rendition of their national anthem by the Austrian band?

25. What sport did Ryan Giggs' dad play?

26. Ray Lewis, the referee who yellow-carded 52 players in the 1992–93 FA Premier League, hails from an appropriately-named place. What is it?

27. Which small Northumberland town is the birthplace of three former Footballers of the Year?

28. Why did both Airdrie and Aberdeen play in their 'away' strips in the Scottish Premier League match of October 1992?

29. Who is the only man to have scored for England against Kuwait?

30. Name the cricket-playing Premier League goalkeeper who once bowled out West Indies star Viv Richards.

31. What is the significance of the green-and-gold halved shirts used by Manchester United as an alternative strip during 1993?

32. What is Des Lynam's favourite team?

33. Which English First Division star quit football in 1969 in order to work full-time as a Jehovah's Witness?

34. Who wrote the football book entitled *The Glory Game*?

35. What unusual occurrence held up the Sampdoria v Pescara Italian League match of May 1993?

36. Name the comedian who is vice-president of Rhyl.

37. What was interesting about the goalkeepers in Preston's 2–1 win over Bury in January 1990?

38. Which club won the 'pie of the season' award from BBC's *Standing Room Only* programme?

39. Which club has a fanzine entitled 'The Adams Family'?

40. In which League did the team known as Abergavenny Thursdays play during 1992–93?

41. What was the title of the film which featured *Lovejoy* star Ian McShane as a soccer player whose career was on the slide?

42. Where is the Sir Norman Chester Centre for Football Research?

43. To what did the headline 'Out Yugo' refer in May 1992?

44. What was the unusual nickname of 1930s Aston Villa striker Thomas Waring?

45. Which member of the Royal Family watched Scotland's World Cup match against Estonia in Tallinn in May 1993?

46. According to the BBC's contract with the Football League during the 1970s, who many Second Division matches had to be shown throughout each season?

47. What occurrence of 1992–93 gave rise to spoof fanzine headlines such as 'Terry Cooper Found on the Moon'?

48. Name three of the famous Englishmen mentioned in Norwegian commentator Borg Lillelien's famous diatribe after his country had defeated England in 1981.

49. For what unusual reason was top Italian amateur referee Silvia Martinetti banned until the end of the 1992–93 season?

50. The wife of which former England international presented *Standing Room Only* during 1992–93?

51. What was the name of the white police horse which played such a starring role in clearing the pitch at the 1923 FA Cup Final – was it Billy, Neddie or Graham?

52. What first did Erik Thorstvedt become in August 1992?

53. Which Scottish First Division club is named after a 7th Century Irish missionary?

54. What happened to Ossie Ardiles' knees in the Spurs' 1981 Cup Final record?

55. Which club's pitch was voted the best in England in 1993?

56. The badge of which former League club now features a phoenix – which represents their comeback from extinction?

57. What connection do Kilmarnock fans have with American singer Marie Osmond?

58. Which FA Premier League club's supporters produce a fanzine entitled 'Red Stripe'?

59. For what unusual reason was goalkeeper John Burridge transfer-listed by Hibs during 1992–93?

60. 'Queen scores late winner at Palace' could have been a headline in the early 1970s. Can you explain how?

How you fared...

46–60	Minutiae Mastermind!
31–45	You know your onions
16–30	Watch more Ceefax!
0–15	Where have you been?

19
NAME THE YEAR

'I made my debut for Partick over 20 years ago and that seems a long time ago now. In many ways though, my career with Liverpool just whizzed by. If I was to pick out one favourite season it would have to be 1978–79. We had a really special team then.'

1. In which year was the FA Cup Final which came to be known as 'The Matthews Final'?

2. Spurs beat Liverpool at Anfield in 1912. When did they next win a League match at The Reds' ground?

3. When was the Football Association founded – 1863, 1873 or 1883?

4. In which year did Watford play in the FA Cup Final for the first and, as yet, only time?

5. Brian Clough was manager of Leeds United for 44 days of which year?

6. When did Manchester United last win the old-style First Division Championship?

7. Ian Rush made his League debut in which year?

8. In which year did Paul Gascoigne win the PFA Young Player of the Year award?

9. When did the Football League adopt three-up and three-down between Divisions One, Two and Three?

10. In which year did Steve Bruce, Brian McClair and Viv Anderson all join Manchester United?

11. Which year saw the first-ever penalty shoot-out in an English first-class match?

12. When did Millwall reach the First Division for the first time in their history?

13. When did Graham Taylor replace Bobby Robson as England boss?

14. In which year was a goal first scored from a penalty-kick – 1871, 1881 or 1891?

15. Gary Lineker joined Spurs and Lou Macari became West Ham manager. Name the year in question.

16. When did *Shoot* magazine first hit the news-stands?

17. In which year did Barclays Bank replace the *Today* newspaper as the sponsors of the Football League?

18. Prior to 1992-93, when was the Scottish 'Treble' last won?

19. When was the first-ever Football League Cup tie played?

20. In which year were substitutes first permitted in Football League matches?

21. When did George Graham become Arsenal manager?

22. In which year did Bobby Charlton play his last League match for Manchester United?

23. When did Southport lose their Football League status – 1972, 1975 or 1978?

24. In which year was the Milk Cup Final contested by two clubs which were eventually relegated?

25. Did the white ball come into official use in 1931, 1941 or 1951?

26. In which year was the FA National School at Lilleshall officially opened – 1984, 1986 or 1988?

27. When did Manchester City first win the League Cup?

28. When did Manchester United first win the League Cup?

29. In which year did Sir Stanley Matthews play his last Football League match?

30. The Fourth Division replaced the Third Divisions North and South, Sunderland were relegated for the first time and Clyde won the Scottish Cup. Name the year.

31. When did Kenny Dalglish become Liverpool's player–manager?

32. Which year witnessed the first-ever Football League matches played on a Sunday?

33. When was the Football League founded?

34. Brazil and England have faced each other three times in the World Cup finals. Can you name the years they met?

35. When did Canon become the first sponsors of the Football League?

36. When did Cardiff City last play in the old-style First Division – 1952, 1962 or 1972?

37. Bill Shankly guided Liverpool to FA Cup success during which year of the 1970s?

38. Aston Villa finished bottom of the First Division and Charlton defeated Leeds in the play-offs. Name the year.

39. In which year were England, Scotland and Wales all represented in European semi-finals?

40. Graeme Souness left Rangers for Liverpool and Luton ended their ban on away fans. When was that?

41. When did Bob Wilson keep goal in his last match for Arsenal?

42. In which year did Don Revie defect as England manager to be succeeded by Ron Greenwood?

43. When did the Milk Cup become the Littlewoods Cup?

44. In which year was the penalty shoot-out introduced into the FA Cup competition?

45. When did Chelsea last win the League Championship?

46. In which year were the FA Cup semi-finals first played on a Sunday and shown 'live' on TV?

47. When did a British club match first net more than £1 million in gate receipts?

48. In which year did Charlie Nicholas win the Scottish Footballer of the Year award?

49. When did Wembley Stadium first stage an England international match – 1920, 1922 or 1924?

50. In which year did Liverpool and Everton draw 4–4 in the fifth round of the FA Cup?

51. Burnley won the Football League, Brian Clough was the Second Division's leading scorer and Hearts were the champions of Scotland. Name the year.

52. When was Britain last completely unrepresented in the quarter-finals of the European tournaments?

53. In which year was the maximum wage abolished in England?

54. When was the first-ever European Cup match played?

55. In which year did Peter Shilton break Bobby Moore's appearance record for England?

56. In which year did a non-League side last win an FA Cup tie away to a First Division club?

57. Ronald Koeman joined Barcelona, Newcastle finished bottom of the First Division and Nigel Clough made his England debut. What was the year?

58. In which year did Trevor Brooking head the winning goal in the FA Cup Final?

59. Ron Atkinson became manager of Cambridge United and Southampton's Mick Channon was the First Division's leading scorer – in which year?

60. When did a Midlands club last win the Championship?

How you fared...

46–60	Year we go!
31–45	Past-master
16–30	Time is on your side
0–15	Back to the future!

20
THAT'S FINAL!

'The FA Cup Final is like a dream to play in – it's the ultimate one-off occasion. I waited a long time to play in the Cup Final at Wembley and I feel strongly that they're devaluing the whole thing nowadays – by playing so many other games there.'

1. Which former Crystal Palace striking partners opposed each other in the 1993 FA Cup Final?

2. Who scored both of West Germany's goals in the 1980 European Championship Final?

3. Which Lancashire club won the first Freight Rover trophy at Wembley in 1985?

4. Which country contested the Final of the Olympic football tournament in 1984 and 1988?

5. Which Englishman helped his team defeat Leeds United in the Final of the 1992 Makita International tournament?

6. Approximately how many people watched the 1993 FA Cup Final replay on TV – 5 million, 10 million or 15 million?

7. How many countries will take part in the final stages of the next European Championships, due to be held in England in 1996?

8. Which was the last team to reach the FA Cup Final and be relegated in the same season?

9. Who scored his 100th goal for Manchester United in the 1992 League Cup Final?

10. In 1993, Finland beat Lithuania 3–0 in the Cup Final of which tournament?

11. Which team reached consecutive Leyland DAF Cup Finals in 1990 and 1991?

12. Which country played in three of the first four European Championship Finals?

13. Which West Country club made back-to-back appearances in the Freight Rover Trophy Final in 1986 and 1987?

14. How many FA Cup Finals did the late Bobby Moore play in?

15. Which country won the one and only replayed European Championship Final?

16. Did Wycombe Wanderers defeat Runcorn, Slough or Telford in the Final of the 1993 Vauxhall FA Trophy?

17. Which team has made the most appearances in the Scottish Cup Final?

18. Who was the only player to pick up a medal at the first match of the 1993 FA Cup Final?

19. Which country defeated Ghana 2–1 in the Final of 1993 FIFA/Coca-Cola World Youth Cup?

20. Why was the FA Cup Final postponed for three weeks in 1963?

21. Which was the last ground other than Wembley to stage a League Cup Final?

22. Which Soviet striker hit the post and had a penalty saved with successive touches of the ball in the 1988 European Championships Final against Holland?

23. Who scored in both the 1989 FA Cup Final and the 1992 Scottish League Cup Final?

24. In the two-legged 1965 Welsh Cup Final, Cardiff defeated Wrexham 5–1 at home and lost 1–0 away, but still had to replay. Why?

25. In 1980, who became the youngest player to appear in an FA Cup Final when he lined up for West Ham against Arsenal?

26. Bridlington defeated Tiverton 1–0 in the 1993 Final of which FA tournament?

27. Which of these London sides have never appeared in the FA Cup Final – Charlton, Millwall or Wimbledon?

28. Which Scandinavian country did the United Kingdom team defeat 2–0 in the Final of the 1908 Olympic Games football tournament in London?

29. Celtic and which other Scottish club contested the Final of the Coronation Cup – the tournament held to celebrate the accession of Queen Elizabeth in 1953?

30. The 1986 Chelsea v Manchester City Full Members' Cup Final is still the highest-scoring Wembley Final between two League clubs. What was the result?

31. In which stadium was the Final of the 1992 Olympic football tournament held?

32. Who were the last pair of brothers to play together in an FA Cup Final?

33. Why was West Germany's Dittmar Jakobs spoken to by the referee after only one minute of the 1986 World Cup Final?

34. Name either of the two current Premier League clubs which have won the League Cup as a Third Division side.

35. Oxford United's Manor Ground staged the 1993 Women's FA Cup Final. Which Premier League club's ladies team defeated Doncaster Belles to take the trophy?

36. Name the Liverpool full-back who broke a collar-bone after only three minutes of the 1965 FA Cup Final but played on until the end of extra-time.

37. Which team beat Dundalk to win the 1993 FAI Cup Final?

38. Have two Second Division sides ever contested the FA Cup Final?

39. True or false – Bill Shankly played in two FA Cup Finals for Liverpool?

40. Name the Manchester City starlet who fired England's winner in the 1993 UEFA Under-21 Championship Final against France in Toulon.

41. Why was the 1915 FA Cup Final known as the 'Khaki Final'?

42. Alan Ball appeared in the FA Cup Final with which two clubs?

43. When Liverpool beat Spurs in the 1982 Milk Cup Final, the four goals were scored by a Scotsman, an Irishman and a Welshman. Name any two of the players concerned.

44. Who scored in consecutive FA Cup Finals for Spurs during the early 1960s – Danny Blanchflower, Jimmy Greaves or Bobby Smith?

45. In 1970, Swindon Town defeated Napoli 3–0 in the first-ever Final of which tournament?

46. Which two 'Uniteds' contested the Final of the 1993 FA Youth Cup?

47. Scottish international Tommy Hutchison scored for both sides in the 1981 FA Cup Final. Name the teams involved.

48. Approximately how many armchair viewers watched the first-ever fully-televised FA Cup Final in 1938 – 1,000, 10,000 or 100,000?

49. True or false – the Scottish Cup Final has never been held outside of Glasgow?

50. Which Dutchman converted an FA Cup Final penalty in 1983?

51. In 1991, Nicosia defeated Ouzavich in the Final of which competition?

52. What first appeared on players' jerseys in the 1933 FA Cup Final?

53. During the years 1971–74, Wolves appeared in the Final of three tournaments. What were they?

54. Bangor eventually defeated Ards to win the 1993 Irish Cup. How many matches did it take them?

55. How much did the first-ever Wembley FA Cup Final programme cost?

56. Which clubs contested the 1977 League Cup Final – a tie which needed two replays to produce a result?

57. In 1987, who became the first team to defeat Spurs in an FA Cup Final?

58. Arsenal lost two cup finals in the space of five days during May 1980 – what were they?

59. True or false – Lawrie Sanchez, who headed Wimbledon's winner in the 1988 FA Cup Final, was born in Ecuador?

60. Which was the last team to score four goals in the FA Cup Final?

How you fared...	
46–60	Superb spectacle
31–45	Enthralling encounter
16–30	A bit of a let-down
0–15	What a flop!

ANSWERS

1   THE PREMIER LEAGUE

1. Oldham's
2. Mike Walker
3. Brian Deane (for Sheffield United against Manchester United)
4. Leeds
5. Sheffield United
6. Tottenham's
7. Blackburn Rovers
8. No. 8
9. Peter Beardsley
10. Peter Reid

11. Craig Forrest and Frank Yallop
12. Dean Saunders
13. Ronnie Rosenthal
14. Norwich
15. Wimbledon
16. Spurs
17. QPR
18. Rick Parry
19. 15
20. Arsenal

21. David James, Bruce Grobbelaar and Mike Hooper
22. Les Ferdinand
23. Norwich
24. Australian
25. Ian Porterfield
26. He had promised not to celebrate if he scored against his old club
27. Green
28. Bryan Robson
29. Bruce Grobbelaar and Peter Ndlovu
30. Crystal Palace

31. Nottingham Forest v Liverpool
32. Arsenal
33. Niall Quinn
34. Ipswich
35. Everton 2 Liverpool 1 and Liverpool 1 Everton 0
36. Manchester City
37. Matt Le Tissier
38. Graeme Souness
39. Everton
40. Kevin Richardson

41. 30
42. Neville Southall
43. It was negative – i.e. they lost more goals than they scored
44. Middlesbrough
45. Spurs
46. Ian Rush
47. Southampton
48. 1–1
49. Chelsea
50. 1995

51. Andy Turner
52. Yes
53. Lee Sharpe
54. Gary McAllister
55. Stamford Bridge (Chelsea)
56. They have never played in the top flight
57. Everton, who won 3–0 at Old Trafford
58. Mick Harford
59. Sheffield United
60. It was the first-ever 'live' *Monday Night Football* Premier
League match

2   FORWARD THINKING

1. Teddy Sheringham
2. Four
3. Ally McCoist
4. Barcelona and Bayern Munich
5. Geoff Hurst
6. Barnsley
7. Belgium
8. Jimmy Greaves
9. Dean Holdsworth
10. West Ham

11. Roger Hunt
12. Andy Cole
13. Malcolm MacDonald
14. 42
15. Dixie Dean
16. Dion Dublin
17. John Aldridge
18. Denis Law and Kenny Dalglish
19. West Bromwich Albion
20. Brian McClair

21. Bulgarian
22. Eric Cantona
23. Katowice, Poland
24. Mick Quinn
25. Preston
26. Mark Falco
27. Alan Smith
28. Derek Dougan
29. John Byrne
30. Wayne Clarke

31. Wimbledon
32. Brian Clough
33. Kerry Dixon
34. Newcastle
35. Cliff Bastin
36. Mo Johnston
37. Michel Platini
38. Jimmy Greaves
39. Dean Saunders
40. Mike Newell

41. Steve Bull
42. Trevor Francis
43. Sunderland
44. Chris Kiwomya
45. John Charles
46. Manchester City's
47. Tony Woodcock
48. Luther Blissett
49. Liverpool
50. Port Vale

51. Bob Latchford
52. Carlisle
53. A loss of approximately £600,000
54. Ipswich
55. The 1930s (1936)
56. Tony Hateley
57. Brian McClair
58. Coventry and Nottingham Forest
59. Mark Hughes
60. 1985–86

3   THE WORLD CUP

1. Turkey and San Marino
2. Diego Maradona
3. The Azteca Stadium, in Mexico City
4. Brazil
5. Joe Jordan
6. 1982
7. He became the first player to be shown the red card during a finals match
8. Argentina, in 1962
9. Czechoslovakia, Hungary and Holland
10. North Korea

11. Holland, in 1974
12. Roger Milla of Cameroon
13. The Republic of Ireland
14. France
15. 1962
16. Only one – Argentina v West Germany in 1990
17. Paolo Rossi
18. Scotland's 3–1 defeat by Peru
19. Alcide Ghiggia who netted in all of Uruguay's matches in 1950
20. Hillsborough

21. Argentina's Claudio Caniggia
22. Three (gold in 1974, silver in '66 and bronze in '70)
23. Tunisia, who beat Mexico 3–1 in 1978
24. They are the only men to have scored in *two* World Cup Finals
25. Peter Shilton
26. Belgium and Italy
27. 1970
28. Brazil
29. Willy and Rene van de Kerkhof

30. Just Fontaine

31. No. 16
32. They reached the finals without playing a single qualifying match on home soil
33. All 22
34. Italy, in 1934
35. Rivelino
36. Peter Beardsley – Newcastle United
37. Ernst Happel – the Austrian who bossed Holland in 1978
38. 16
39. England 1 West Germany 0
40. Laszlo Kiss

41. Lothar Matthaus
42. Turin and Bari
43. Socrates
44. Czechoslovakia
45. Mark Hughes
46. Italy
47. They were the official mascots of the tournaments
48. 1974
49. Tom Finney
50. Yugoslavia

51. Greece
52. Black
53. The wave
54. Czechoslovakia v Costa Rica
55. Three
56. Brazil and Hungary
57. All 22
58. France and Belgium
59. Daniel Passarella in 1978
60. Diego Maradona

4   CLUB CALL

1. Charlton
2. Jack Walker
3. Seven
4. Crewe Alexandra
5. Manchester City
6. Newcastle United
7. Harry Hampton
8. Tranmere Rovers
9. Preston
10. Maidstone

11. The 1950s
12. Derby County
13. Barrow
14. No
15. The European Cup-Winners' Cup
16. Peterborough United
17. False, they've won it twice
18. Leicester City
19. Accrington Stanley
20. Derby County

21. Blackpool and Manchester United
22. The 1920s
23. Swansea
24. Oldham
25. The sixth round
26. Wolves
27. Aston Villa
28. Ray Clemence
29. Port Vale
30. Swindon

31. Crewe
32. Tottenham
33. Wednesday
34. Chairman Doug Ellis
35. Cwmbran Town
36. Stoke
37. The Glaziers
38. Nat Lofthouse
39. Lincoln City
40. Claret and white

41. Burnley
42. Portsmouth
43. Don Howe
44. AFC Bournemouth
45. Bristol City
46. Bradford Park Avenue
47. Spurs
48. Yes
49. Millwall
50. None

51. Sunderland
52. Swansea Town
53. Reading
54. Wolves
55. 1987
56. Arsenal
57. Darlington
58. Dai Davies
59. City
60. Wimbledon

5   SOCCER IN EUROPE

1. Deportivo
2. Bruges
3. Holland
4. Gianluigi Lentini (Milan)
5. Dynamo Kiev
6. Swiss
7. Anderlecht
8. Monaco
9. PSV Eindhoven
10. Lars Olsen

11. Rune Bratseth
12. John Toshack
13. Kopa, Platini and Papin
14. Ajax Amsterdam
15. AEK Athens
16. Denmark
17. Real Zaragoza
18. Franz Beckenbauer
19. Hristo Stoichkov
20. Ferencvaros

21. Luxembourg
22. Gelsenkirchen
23. Basile Boli
24. Estonia
25. Seville
26. Their team comprises only amateur players
27. Sweden
28. Benfica
29. Feyenoord and Sparta
30. Terry Venables

31. Paris Saint-Germain
32. Lajos Detari
33. Roy Hodgson
34. The Heysel Stadium in Brussels
35. Matthias Sammer
36. Malta
37. Tahiti
38. Portugal
39. Gothenburg
40. Dynamo Berlin

41. Hans van Breukelen
42. Greece
43. Belgium
44. It was he who thought up the name Grasshoppers for the Zurich club
45. Ajax, Feyenoord and Barcelona
46. A penalty shoot-out
47. Juventus
48. Rayo Vallecano
49. Oleg Blokhin
50. Switzerland

51. Bayern
52. Michel
53. It is the date of the country's National Liberation Day (17th November)
54. Stockholm
55. John de Wolf
56. Switzerland
57. Cologne
58. Romania
59. Tenerife
60. Bochum

6   ENGLAND: THE TEAM

1. Les Ferdinand
2. The USA
3. Brian and Nigel Clough
4. 48
5. Bryan Robson
6. Third, in 1968
7. Gerry Hitchens
8. Jan Wouters
9. 1991
10. Alan Ball

11. Rodney Marsh
12. Santander, Spain
13. Paul Ince
14. Brazil
15. 'The Lion of Vienna'
16. Bobby Moore
17. An Achilles' tendon injury
18. Four
19. Stuart Pearce
20. 0–0

21. Kevin Keegan
22. Twice (1974 and 1978)
23. Seven (from Arsenal, v Italy in 1934)
24. None
25. Duncan Edwards
26. Ron Greenwood
27. They all have
28. Roger Hunt
29. 6–3
30. Steve Bull

31. Nobby Stiles
32. Jimmy Greaves
33. 1984
34. Gordon Banks
35. None
36. Southampton
37. Ray Houghton
38. 1955
39. Bryan Robson
40. Walter Winterbottom

41. Portsmouth, Milan, Monaco and Rangers
42. Denmark
43. Bobby Moore
44. Pierluigi Benedettini
45. Viv Anderson
46. They were all born outside of the UK
47. The Republic of Ireland
48. Alan Hodgkinson
49. Stuart Pearce and Chris Waddle
50. 7–0 (to England!)

51. David White
52. Gerd Muller's
53. Peter Shilton
54 Nigel Martyn
55. Joe Baker
56. Twice
57. Paul Merson and Martin Keown
58. Ewood Park (Crompton played for Blackburn Rovers)
59. Alf Ramsey
60. Middlesbrough

7   CUP CRAZY

1. John Harkes
2. Liverpool, in 1988 and 1989
3. False, since 1967
4. The Wanderers
5. Alan Smith
6. He became the first referee to send a player off in an FA Cup Final
7. Rochdale
8. Gary Lineker
9. Newcastle United
10. Oxford United

11. Liverpool
12. Gary Bailey
13. Steve McManaman
14. QPR in 1967
15. Wolves
16. Trevor Cherry and Peter Lorimer
17. Crystal Palace
18. Norman Whiteside
19. Kennington Oval and Crystal Palace`
20. Danny Wilson

21. Hartlepool
22. Twice
23. He scored the winning goal but suffered a broken arm in an accident during the after-match celebrations
24. West Bromwich Albion
25. Bolton
26. Andy Gray
27. Sheffield United
28. George Graham
29. Leicester
30. Norman Whiteside

31. Paul Warhurst

32. Peter Osgood

33. On the wing after being badly injured in a collision with Aston Villa's Peter McParland

34. Maine Road, Manchester City

35. Blyth Spartans

36. The Kingstonian goalkeeper had been knocked out by a missile when the score was 3–0

37. Frank Stapleton

38. Brian Clough

39. Chelsea and Leeds

40. Ian Callaghan

41. Nottingham Forest and Norwich City

42. They reached the Final

43. Old Etonians in 1882

44. George and Ted Robledo

45. Blackburn Rovers

46. Arsenal

47. They have scored the goal(s) which eliminated the holders

48. Bobby Robson

49. No

50. He became the first man to have skippered three winning teams

51. Newcastle

52. Liverpool and Nottingham Forest

53. Stanley Rous

54. 1982 (Spurs v QPR)

55. They lost 8–0

56. Chris Waddle

57. False

58. The German airship *Graf Zeppelin*

59. Stoke City

60. Six

8   SUPER STOPPERS

1. Torben Piechnik
2. True
3. David O'Leary
4. Bobby Moore
5. Colin Hendry
6. Steve Foster
7. Northern Ireland
8. Leeds
9. Brian Kilcline
10. Paul McGrath

11. Tottenham
12. Chris Whyte and Chris Fairclough
13. Paul Elliott's
14. Des Walker
15. Jeff Blockley
16. A head-band
17. Steve Bruce
18. David Nish
19. Chelsea
20. Tommy Smith

21. Mal Donaghy
22. Oxford United
23. George Berry
24. Gunnar Halle
25. 1990 – Crystal Palace v Manchester United
26. Wolves
27. Martin Buchan
28. Wales
29. Rangers
30. Andy Linighan

31. Brian Labone
32. Malmo
33. Dave Watson and Gary Ablett
34. Norman Hunter
35. Andy Brehme (West Germany)
36. Southampton
37. Bill Foulkes
38. 1975
39. Billy Bonds
40. QPR

41. False
42. Paul Bodin
43. Sporting Gijon
44. All four (he scored two own goals)
45. Nicky Reid
46. Billy Wright
47. Alan Kennedy
48. Ken McNaught and Alan Evans
49. Des Walker
50. Twice

51. Kenny Burns
52. Holland
53. Neil Franklin
54. Phil Thompson
55. Ron Flowers
56. Bournemouth
57. Terry Neill
58. Franz Beckenbauer
59. 1978
60. Mike Doyle

9   ALL CHANGE

1. Roy Wegerle
2. It was the first £500,000-plus deal between two British clubs
3. Less than a year
4. Brian Gayle, Keith Curle and Terry Phelan
5. Ayr United
6. March
7. Nottingham Forest
8. Darren Anderton
9. CSKA Moscow
10. 19

11. Roy and Pat Keane
12. Terry Venables
13. David Jack
14. Kenny Sansom
15. France
16. Anders Limpar
17. £3.3 million
18. Brian Clough
19. Gary Pallister
20. Kenny Dalglish

21. Five weeks
22. John Jensen
23. Joe Jordan
24. Mark Falco, Graham Roberts and Richard Gough
25. Andy Gray
26. The players involved were brothers – Ron and Peter Springett
27. Ray Houghton
28. Millwall
29. Garry Birtles and Neil Webb
30. Leeds

31. Norwich
32. Graeme Souness
33. Ferguson's fifth Scotland appearance meant that The Saints received an extra £50,000 as a result of a clause in the transfer contract when he was sold to Rangers in 1988
34. Tow Law Town
35. Tony Cascarino
36. Bolton, Everton and QPR
37. Jimmy Greaves
38. £1.3 million
39. John Sheridan
40. Five (QPR, Arsenal, Crystal Palace, Chelsea and West Ham)

41. Efan Ekoku
42. Colombia
43. £54 million
44. Spurs
45. Tony Cottee
46. Eddie Firmani
47. Arsenal
48. Marco Gabbiadini
49. Ray Wilkins
50. £1.5 million

51. Crystal Palace
52. Laurie Cunningham
53. He was the first player to be transferred for £1,000
54. Frank Stapleton
55. Steve Daley
56. Rod and Ray Wallace
57. Celtic
58. Alexei Mikhailichenko (Rangers)
59. True
60. £3.25 million

10   FOOTBALL ITALIA

1. AC Milan
2. Sunday
3. Inter Milan
4. BSB (British Satellite Broadcasting)
5. Paul Gascoigne
6. It is played over two home-and-away legs
7. Roberto and Dino
8. Florence
9. Roma and Torino
10. Paul Rideout, Gordon Cowans and David Platt

11. Cremonese
12. Their colours – they all play in blue-and-black striped shirts
13. Karlheinz Riedle
14. The championship shield
15. Gianluca Vialli
16. Cagliari
17. The *Azzurri* (Blues)
18. Sampdoria
19. Giuseppe Signori
20. Franco Baresi

21. 1986
22. Naples
23. Atalanta
24. Juventus
25. One
26 Stefan Effenberg and Brian Laudrup
27. San Siro
28. Pasquale Bruno
29. No. 10
30. 1893

31. Luigi Riva
32. Arrigo Sacchi
33. The FIGC (*Federazione Italiana Giuoco Calcio*)
34. Milan's 58-game and 17-month unbeaten run
35. Gianluca Pagliuca
36. A midfielder
37. Carnevale and Caniggia
38. Atalanta's
39. 1–1
40. Sampdoria

41. A carbon mask to protect his fractured cheek-bone
42. Torino
43. Dino Zoff
44. Napoli
45. Inter Milan
46. Gheorghe Hagi
47. Boban, Savicevic and Papin
48. Milan and Juventus
49. Fiorentina
50. Because both clubs were originally founded by Englishmen

51. Thomas Hassler
52. Fiorentina
53. True
54. Foggia
55. Franco Baresi
56. It was pointed out that the patterns on the jerseys looked like Nazi-style swastikas
57. Roberto Falcao
58. Sampdoria v Lazio
59. Liam Brady
60. All his goals came from penalties

11   LAWS OF THE GAME

1. False, he must merely stand on the goal-line
2. No
3. An indirect free-kick
4. He is indicating that the player has committed a second cautionable offence and is therefore being ordered off
5. False – they must wait for the ball to be kicked
6. Yes providing the referee is informed and that play is stopped
7. Eight feet
8. He would be wrong to do so since the ball had not travelled its own circumference and therefore, technically, the kick was not taken
9. False – it should be awarded to the opposing team
10. Only if foul and abusive language was involved

11. Officially, they are obliged to wear colours which distinguish them from other players and also from the referee (who wear green in the Premier League)
12. He must decide at which end the kicks will be taken
13. False – by a direct free-kick
14. The kicks can now be taken from either side of the six-yard box
15. Yes, but he should be allowed to return if he has donned acceptable footwear
16. That is the regulation pressure of the ball at the start of the match
17. Send the offending player off and restart play with the corner-kick
18. Handling the ball
19. Yes, providing that the game has not been restarted
20. When the pitch is covered in snow

21. Yes
22. Yes, providing the referee decides that it doesn't constitute a danger to other players

23. Yes

24. False

25. 120

26. Yes, as long as the referee is happy that the colours are distinct (Chelsea wore their normal blue shirts at Manchester City in September 1992)

27. Award a goal – other players are only required to be on the field, outside of the penalty-area

28. Yes, but not by stopping his kicking action

29. False, in some cases it could be smaller

30. Order him from the field until the blood flow is stemmed and the wound covered up

31. Yes, providing all the usual substitution criteria are met

32. Neither, the kick should be re-taken

33. False, any player (including the goalkeepers) who was on the field at the end of the match may take a kick

34. A goal-kick

35. Yes, so long as there's still no colour clash with the opponents

36. Only if he considers that the opposition have been intentionally denied a 'clear goalscoring opportunity' by the goalkeeper's action

37. Yes, a long throw out from the goalkeeper would score if it carried that far

38. Yes, providing all the other players in his team have taken one

39. No, players have the right to an interval

40. Yes. If they kick-off after conceding a first-half equalizer, kick-off again at the start of the second half and, assuming the match goes into extra-time, win the toss to start the extra period

41. No, the free-kick would be taken on the six-yard line

42. No, the referee should award a corner-kick

43. The centre circle

44. A penalty-kick

45. Yes, the referee may well deem that acceptable, especially in very cold conditions

46. In the case of the corner-flag, yes. However, if it hits the half-way flag, it has gone out of play and a throw-in should be awarded

47. Shinguards

48. True – assuming that their opponents have missed their first three

49. The 'professional foul'

50. False – the passes themselves are not illegal but the goalkeeper may not now handle a ball which has been deliberately kicked to him by a team-mate

51. Yes

52. By an indirect free-kick to opposing team from the spot where the offence occurred

53. After 1990, an attacker could not be offside if he was level with the last outfield defender when the ball was played (previously, he had to be nearer his own goal to be onside)

54. Yes, if the charge is fair, i.e. with the shoulder, and the opponent is obstructing

55. 120 yards

56. It is up to the referee to decide what constitutes time-wasting – no particular length of time is specified in the rules

57. Yes, the law merely requires that it weighs no more than that at the start of the match

58. Only if the referee is certain that no opponents were distracted or misled by the shout

59. Five feet

60. No, unless the referee considers that he was seeking to gain an advantage by returning quickly to the field from such a position

12   SCOTTISH FOOTBALL

1. Aberdeen
2. Jim McLean
3. Celtic's European Cup winning side of 1967 (they won the trophy in Lisbon)
4. Maroon and white
5. Dundee United
6. Gary McAllister (for Leeds)
7. Six
8. Kevin Ratcliffe
9. Hearts
10. Stenhousemuir

11. Alexei Mikhailichenko (with Dynamo Kiev and Sampdoria)
12. 1983
13. Hibs and Hearts
14. Ally McCoist
15. Jimmy Nicholl
16. They were the double glazing firm which sponsored both clubs' jerseys
17. Simon Stainrod
18. Hearts
19. Tony Parks
20. East Fife, East Stirlingshire and Queen of the South

21. Arbroath
22. No
23. Raith Rovers
24. Jimmy Millar and Ralph Brand
25. They were accused of re-scheduling fixtures in order to field players who would otherwise have been suspended
26. Celtic and Albion Rovers
27. A large red 'diamond' which runs from the front over to the back
28. Stuart Slater

29. Alex Ferguson and Andy Roxburgh
30. Andy Goram

31. Dunfermline, Cowdenbeath, Raith Rovers and East Fife
32. Colin Miller
33. Hibs
34. Aberdeen
35. Richard Gough
36. Meadowbank Thistle
37. The Adidas Golden Boot for Europe's leading league scorer
38. Hibs
39. Hearts
40. Dundee United

41. Partick Thistle
42. Aberdeen and Rangers
43. Davie Hay
44. Justin Fashanu
45. FC Twente Enschede
46. 18
47. Tommy Burns and Billy Stark
48. True
49. Hibs
50. Roddy Forsyth

51. Sandy Clark
52. Brechin
53. Neil Murray
54. Third
55. St Mirren and Falkirk
56. Ian McMillan
57. Albion Rovers
58. Four
59. Dundee
60. Richard Gough

13   FACTS AND FEATS

1. Eric Cantona
2. Nottingham Forest
3. Five
4. Spurs
5. Jason Dozzell
6. Celtic
7. 9–3
8. Nine
9. Rangers
10. Grimsby

11. Ted Drake
12. Two
13. Cowdenbeath
14. Arsenal
15. Bob Paisley
16. Manchester City in 1957–58
17. He was the subject of the fastest-ever sending-off in the World Cup finals
18. Dariusz Dziekanowski – for Celtic against Partizan Belgrade
19. Stockport
20. Phil Neal

21. He is the League's highest all-time scorer
22. Hungary
23. York City
24. Sporting Lisbon
25. Preston
26. Johnny Haynes
27. Stan Cullis
28. Shamrock Rovers
29. 34
30. Northampton Town

31. Arsenal

32. Leeds and Liverpool

33. Ireland

34. Sir Stanley Matthews

35. Wimbledon and Luton

36. The Second Division

37. Eight

38. Peter Shilton

39. Milan, Penarol and Nacional

40. John Aldridge

41. Coventry City

42. No, the official British record crowd is the 149,547 who saw Scotland beat England in 1937. However probably more than that number squeezed into Wembley for the 1923 FA Cup Final

43. John Aldridge

44. They were all scored in the First Division

45. Pat Jennings

46. Celtic

47. 45

48. 14 (by Liverpool in1965–66 and Aston Villa in 1980–81)

49. Crystal Palace

50. England's

51. Ryan Giggs

52. Spurs, who beat Bristol Rovers 9–0 in October 1977

53. They became the first British club to have four players ordered off in a first-class match

54. Seven

55. Northern Ireland

56. He was the first player to be ordered off

57. Brian Talbot

58. Five

59. Frank Stapleton

60. David Kelly (Walsall)

14   STADIA STATS

1. White Hart Lane
2. The Prater Stadium
3. Newcastle's St James' Park
4. Parkhead (Celtic Park)
5. Kenny Dalglish
6. QPR
7. There were complaints that the painted-on fans didn't include any ethnic minorities
8. Birmingham City
9. Old Trafford
10. Dortmund's Westfalenstadion

11. Anfield
12. Cardiff City
13. Shielfield Park, Berwick
14. Lansdowne Road
15. Maine Road
16. Yes
17. The Boat Race
18. Watling Street, Dartford
19. Celtic
20. Stranraer's Stair Park

21. Boothferry Park, Hull
22. Hampden Park
23. The old Crystal Palace
24. Arbroath's Gayfield Park
25. The Valley
26. Carlisle's Brunton Park
27. Install floodlights
28. Dens Park (Dundee) and Tannadice Park (Dundee United)
29 'The Tub'
30. Wrexham

31. The City Ground, Nottingham Forest
32. Cricket
33. Brussels
34. Scunthorpe
35. Villa Park
36. Elland Road
37. Ibrox and Pittodrie
38. Exeter
39. Old Trafford – where Argentina met the USSR in 1991
40. 100,000 attended the 1953 FA Amateur Cup Final between Pegasus and Harwich & Parkeston

41. Cumbernauld
42. Belgrade
43. Northern Ireland
44. Old Trafford
45. Toulouse
46. 1990
47. Chester
48. 'You'll Never Walk Alone'
49. Wimbledon and Oldham
50. Priestfield Stadium, Gillingham

51. Plymouth's
52. Three
53. Portsmouth
54. Highbury
55. Highfield Road
56. US troops
57. Newport County
58. 1896
59. Chester
60. It was converted into a seating area

15 THE EUROPEAN CUPS

1. Basile Boli
2. Real Madrid
3. Georges Grun
4. Ally McCoist
5. Panathinaikos
6. Stuttgart had broken UEFA regulations by fielding four foreign players in their side
7. Tottenham
8. Moscow – against Torpedo
9. Marco van Basten
10. Liverpool

11. Germany
12. Kevin Keegan
13. The semi-finals
14. Red Star Belgrade
15. 1987–88
16. Manchester United
17. Voller (Marseille), Moller and Kohler (Juventus)
18. Paris
19. Mark Hateley
20. They have each managed two different clubs to European Cup-Winners' Cup victory

21. Anderlecht, Standard Liege and KV Mechelen
22. Paul Breitner
23. Stuart McCall (for Rangers)
24. Real Madrid
25. The Fairs Cup
26. Ajax Amsterdam
27. They swapped the orange jerseys they had worn during the match for Barca's traditional blue-and-red striped tops
28. Ten
29. Robbie Resenbrink

30. They were contested as one-off matches

31. Arsenal

32. They have all hosted recent Cup-Winners' Cup Finals?

33. All blue in 1968 and all white in 1991

34. FC Magdeburg, Carl Zeiss Jena and Lokomotiv Leipzig

35. Ipswich and Leeds

36. Stamford Bridge

37. The referee had signalled that the free-kick was indirect but still allowed the goal

38. Liverpool and Leeds

39. The late goal from Cologne's Japanese substitute Okudera which earned the Germans a 3–3 draw at Nottingham Forest's City Ground in the first leg of the European Cup semi-final

40. Lothar Matthaus

41. Ferencvaros

42. Marco van Basten

43. Rotterdam

44. Peter Lorimer

45. Five

46. Glentoran

47. No

48. John Robertson

49. Paris Saint-Germain and Auxerre

50. Uli Stielike

51. Spurs

52. European Cup-Winners' Cup

53. False – they lost a play-off against the first winners Barcelona

54. Espanol

55. Phil Neal and Paul Walsh

56. Kaiserslautern

57. Newcastle United

58. Videoton

59. Ray Kennedy

60. Dundee United, Manchester United, Aberdeen and Nottingham Forest

16   THE GAFFERS

1. Joe Royle
2. Terry Venables
3. Lawrie McMenemy
4. The 1990 FA Cup
5. 1991
6. Tommy Docherty
7. Danny Bergara
8. Bob Paisley
9. Lennie Lawrence
10. Southend

11. Bill Nicholson
12. Chelsea
13. Jock Wallace
14. PSV Eindhoven
15. Malcolm Allison
16. Dave Mackay
17. Joe Kinnear
18. Howard Kendall and Harry Catterick
19. Sir Alf Ramsey
20. Clyde

21. Ron Saunders
22. Bob Stokoe
23. Bob Paisley
24. Huddersfield Town and Bolton Wanderers
25. He scored a hat-trick against Aston Villa
26. Graham Taylor
27. Ally MacLeod ('Ally's Tartan Army')
28. Peter Shilton
29. Notts County
30. Port Vale

31. Dave Sexton

32. Nine
33. John Beck
34. Exeter City
35. Brian Kidd
36. Dave Stringer
37. Cambridge United
38. False – he is a Scottish international
39. Terry Butcher
40. Chelsea

41. Bill Shankly
42. Bobby Houghton (Malmo) and Brian Clough (Nottingham Forest)
43. Bobby Gould
44. Alf Ramsey
45. He wanted his side to emulate the feats of the legendary white-clad Real Madrid
46. Keith Burkinshaw
47. He was part of the Sky Sports production team
48. Bruce Rioch
49. Simon Stainrod
50. Athletic Bilbao

51. Ivan Golac
52. Graham Taylor
53. Billy Bremner
54. Brian Clough
55. Six
56. National coach
57. Coventry City
58. Berti Mee
59. Howard Wilkinson
60. Terry Venables

17 AT HOME AND ABROAD

1. 1992
2. The Ivory Coast
3. Tangerine
4. Sierra Leone
5. The Anglo–Scottish Cup
6. North and Central America and the Caribbean
7. Leyton Orient
8. Inter Milan
9. True
10. Chile

11. The Football Grounds Improvement Trust
12. It was watched by the largest crowd ever to attend a club match
13. Rochdale
14. Nagoya
15. The old Second Division
16. Northern Ireland
17. QPR
18. Argentina
19. St Johnstone
20. Guadalajara

21. Rockingham Road
22. Zico
23. Orient
24. They feared an American attack on their controversial chemical plant
25. Merthyr Tydfil
26. Uruguay
27. True
28. The All-Whites
29. Three
30. Chile

31. Oldham
32. Ghana
33. Ray Wilkins
34. Gordon Strachan
35. Ian Porterfield and Mark McGhee
36. Buenos Aires
37. The Diadora League Premier Division
38. False, he was born in Amsterdam but had a Surinamese father
39. Gordon Banks
40. 1970

41. Barnet
42. They have the world's highest senior football ground – 4,350 metres above sea-level
43. The Beazer Homes Southern League
44. Vasco da Gama
45. Stuart Pearce
46. Liberia
47. Wrexham
48. France
49. The pitch has a pronounced slope on it
50. Namibia

51. Leyton Orient
52. Cairo
53. Northwich Victoria
54. Italy
55. No
56. None
57. Bristol Rovers
58. The Giants Stadium
59. The 1968 FA Cup
60. No, they withdrew before the start

18 TRIVIA TEASERS

1. He was the dog who found the World Cup trophy after it had been stolen in London in 1966
2. Wycombe Wanderers
3. Monday
4. Derby County (he was better known as Robert Maxwell!)
5. It was the first game ever shown on *Match of the Day*
6. Vinnie Jones
7. To celebrate the club's eighth successive League Championship, won the previous season
8. Sylvester Stallone
9. It's a throw-back to their origins. West Ham's father club was Thames Ironworks FC and the hammers represent the shipyard tools
10. Players who performed near-choreographed dance routines after scoring

11. They wrote the words and music of the hymn 'Abide With Me' which is traditionally sung before the match
12. Liverpool
13. Kevin Francis
14. He persuaded the referee to give a penalty against his own team
15. Roy of the Rovers
16. Roberto Baggio
17. Stan Bowles
18. Eric Cantona
19. Nottingham Forest
20. He was the official UEFA mascot for the 1992 European Championship

21. They confiscated their boots if they had metal toe-caps
22. Carlisle chairman Michael Knighton who had previously made an unsuccessful attempt to take control of Manchester United

23. Peterborough
24. Bulgaria, whose manager claimed it was a calculated move to make his players angry and therefore cause them to lose their composure
25. Rugby League
26. Great Bookham
27. Ashington (Jackie Milburn and the Charlton brothers)
28. Visitors Aberdeen mistakenly brought only their white away strip which clashed with Airdrie's regular kit, forcing the home side to change into *their* away strip
29. Trevor Francis
30. Steve Ogrizovic

31. These were the colours of Newton Heath – the club which eventually became Manchester United
32. Brighton
33. Peter Knowles
34. Hunter Davies
35. A swarm of 20,000 bees had settled in one of the goals
36. Stan Boardman
37. They were brothers – Gary and Alan Kelly
38. Notts County
39. Wycombe Wanderers
40. The Konica League of Wales

41. *Yesterday's Hero*
42. Leicester University
43. Yugoslavia's expulsion from the European Championships
44. Pongo
45. The Duke of Kent
46. Fourteen
47. The take-over of Birmingham City by *Sunday Sport* publisher David Sullivan
48. Lord Nelson, Lord Beaverbrook, Winston Churchill, Henry Cooper, Clement Atlee and Anthony Eden
49. *She* was pregnant
50. Neil Webb

51. Billy
52. He became the Premier League's first substitute goalkeeper when he replaced Ian Walker against Coventry
53. St Mirren
54. They went 'all trembly' (Because he was going to Wembley!)
55. Wolves
56. Aldershot
57. Her big hit 'Paper Roses' is a popular terracing song at Kilmarnock's Rugby Park
58. Southampton's
59. His refusal to wear a particular make of jersey because it was 'too sticky'
60. Crystal Palace had, at that time, a striker called Gerry Queen

19   NAME THE YEAR

1. 1953
2. 1985
3. 1863
4. 1984
5. 1974
6. 1967
7. 1979
8. 1988
9. 1973 (it first applied in 1974)

10. 1987
11. 1970 (in the Watney Cup tournament)
12. 1988
13. 1990
14. 1891
15. 1989
16. 1969
17. 1987
18. 1978
19. 1960
20. 1965

21. 1986
22. 1973
23. 1978
24. 1985
25. 1951
26. 1984
27. 1970
28. 1992
29. 1965
30. 1958

31. 1985
32. 1974
33. 1888
34. 1958, 1962 and 1970
35. 1983
36. 1962
37. 1974
38. 1987
39. 1968
40. 1991

41. 1974
42. 1977
43. 1986
44. 1991
45. 1955
46. 1990
47. 1985 (the FA Cup Final)
48. 1983
49. 1924
50. 1991

51. 1960
52. 1990
53. 1961
54. 1955
55. 1989
56. 1986 (Altrincham won at Birmingham City)
57. 1989
58. 1980
59. 1974
60. 1981 (Aston Villa)

20   THAT'S FINAL!

1. Ian Wright and Mark Bright
2. Horst Hrubesch
3. Wigan
4. Brazil
5. Des Walker
6. 15 million
7. Sixteen
8. Brighton
9. Brian McClair
10. The Baltic Cup

11. Tranmere
12. The USSR
13. Bristol City
14. Two (for West Ham and Fulham)
15. Italy
16. Runcorn
17. Celtic
18. Steve Morrow, who belatedly received his Coca-Cola Cup medal
19. Brazil
20. The severe winter had caused a backlog of fixtures

21. Maine Road
22. Igor Belanov
23. Stuart McCall
24. The Final was decided on points
25. Paul Allen
26. The FA Challenge Vase
27. Millwall
28. Denmark
29. Hibs
30. Chelsea 5 Manchester City 4
31. The Nou Camp in Barcelona

32. Jimmy and Brian Greenhoff (Manchester United 1977)
33. He was instructed to pull his socks up to comply with FIFA regulations
34. QPR and Swindon
35. Arsenal Ladies
36. Gerry Byrne
37. Shelbourne
38. No
39. False – he was with Preston North End at the time
40. Gary Flitcroft

41. Because it took place during wartime and was attended by many servicemen (in khaki uniforms)
42. Everton and Arsenal
43. Ronnie Whelan, Ian Rush and Steve Archibald
44. Bobby Smith
45. The Anglo–Italian Cup
46. Manchester United and Leeds
47. Manchester City and Spurs
48. 10,000
49. False
50. Arnold Muhren

51. The FA Sunday Cup
52. Numbers
53. The Texaco Cup, the UEFA Cup and the Football League Cup
54. Three
55. Three old pence (approximately one and a quarter pence today)
56. Aston Villa and Everton
57. Coventry
58. The FA Cup and the European Cup-Winners' Cup
59. False
60. Manchester United